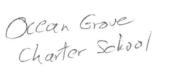

W9-CTB-983

Table of Contents

Using this Guide

This book is a *guide* for teachers using the *Primary Mathematics* curriculum. It is designed to help teachers understand the course material, see how each section fits in with the curriculum as a whole, and prepare the day's lesson. The course material is divided into 80 sessions. Sessions can be combined for one day's lesson, if necessary to finish the curriculum by then end of the semester, by spending less time on class participation or discussion or not having as many problems for practice during class time.

This guide is designed to be used with both the U.S. edition and the third edition of *Primary Mathematics*. U.S. conventions and spellings are used in this guide, such as using commas for thousands and colons for time, and not using "and" in writing out whole numbers in words. However, any items specific to either edition, such as different answers, different page numbers, and different exercise numbers, are clearly indicated.

This guide includes some worksheets, which can be copied for single class use only.

Workbook exercises can be gone over in class or assigned as homework.

Suggested Material

Counters
Use some kind of counters that can be displayed, such as transparent counters with an overhead projector or something that can be stuck on the board and moved around. Students will also need counters of different colors for some of the games.

Number cubes
This is a cube that can be labeled with different numbers. You need enough for each group of students to have two number cubes. 10-sided dice could also be used.

Counting sticks, craft sticks, or straws that can be bundled into tens with rubber bands or tape. These will only be used in the first few lessons. Students can also make groups of tens from multi-link cubes, but they should realize that any object can be grouped into tens, not just objects designed for math classes.

Hundreds board
This is a chart with squares in a 10 x 10 array numbered from 1 to 100. Have one that can be displayed, such as one for the overhead projector, or one drawn on a poster. You will also need to display a blank hundreds board, or a 10 x 10 array but without numbers in the squares. Each student should have a laminated or paper hundreds board with spaces large enough to be covered up by counters.

Place-value chart
Each student should have a reusable place-value chart with three columns for hundreds, tens, and ones. They can be made on thin cardboard and placed within a plastic sleeve protector so that students can write on them with dry-erase markers, or lines can be drawn on personal-sized white boards. If you are using number discs (see below) the place-value charts should be large enough to place discs on and move them around.

Number discs

These are discs with 1, 10, and 100 written on them. Have some that can be displayed; you can write the numbers on transparent counters if you have an overhead projector, or make some cardboard ones with a sticky or magnetic back. You can also simply draw circles on the board and label them. For student manipulatives, you can write the numbers on opaque counters. Each student or group of students should have 18 of each type. Though discs students can handle can make the lesson more concrete, it can also be time consuming. To save time, students could also draw circles on their place-value chart. If they do so, they do not have to write the 1, 10, or 100 in each circle representing a disc; the column the disc is placed in indicates its value.

Base-10 blocks

A set with unit cubes, rods (10 units), flats (10 rods), and a cube (10 flats). Use ones that can be displayed from the front of the class (such as using an overhead projector or ones that can be stuck onto the board). You can also draw them on the board, but students should be familiar with the concrete objects your drawing represents.

Number cubes

This is a cube that can be labeled, using a sticker, with a different number on each side. You need enough for each group of students to have 4 number cubes. 10-sided dice could also be used.

Number cards

You will need various number cards for games or group activities. You can use index cards, but make sure that the number does not show through the card. Many activities will call for four sets of number cards 0-9 for each group. These can be made from playing cards by removing the face cards, making the Ace a 1, and whiting out the 1 and the symbols for the 10 to make them 0. You can also write the numbers on blank playing cards. Such cards will be easier to handle than index cards.

Connect-a-cubes

These cubes can be connected on all six sides. There should be enough for each group of students to have about 100. Geo-shapes are available that can also be connected to each other and to the cubes and are used in some optional activities.

Measuring tools

Rulers, meter sticks, yard sticks, balances, scales.

Fact cards

Cards with multiplication facts for twos and threes, with the expression on one side and the answer on the back for individual fact practice. Students can also work in pairs to drill each other, or use the cards at home. Students can make their own cards with index paper and crayons.

You will also need a set of fact cards without the answers on the back and separate cards with answers to play some of the games.

Optional Resources

Extra Practice for Primary Mathematics 2 (U.S. Edition)
This workbook has two to four page exercises covering topics from *Primary Mathematics 2A* and *Primary Mathematics 2B*. The level of difficulty and format of the problems is similar to that of the *Primary Mathematics*. Answers are in the back.

Primary Mathematics Challenging Word Problems 2 (U.S. Edition)
This workbook has word problems only. The problems are topically arranged, with the topics following the same sequence as *Primary Mathematics 2A* and *2B*. Each topic starts with three worked examples, followed by practice problems and then challenge problems. Although the computation skills needed to solve the problems is at the same level as the corresponding *Primary Mathematics*, the problem solving techniques necessary in the challenge section are sometimes more advanced than needed for the problems in the textbook or workbook, and the problems sometimes require more than one step to solve. It is a good source, though, of extra word problems that can be discussed in class or of enrichment problems for more capable students. Answers are in the back.

Primary Mathematics Intensive Practice 2A (U.S. Edition)
This supplemental workbook has one set of problems for each topic in *Primary Mathematics*. Each topical exercise has questions of varying levels of difficulty, but the difficulty level is usually higher than that in the *Primary Mathematics* textbook or workbook. Some of the word problems are quite challenging and require the students to extend their understanding of the concepts and to develop problem solving abilities. Students may not be able to solve all the problems in this section independently even if they have a good understanding of the concepts due to the advanced problem-solving required. There is also a section called "Take the Challenge!" with non-routine problems that can be used to further develop students' problem solving abilities. Answers are located in the back.

Rainbow Rock CD-ROM
Rainbow Rock CD-ROM won the Bronze World Medal in the 1999 New York Festivals International Interactive Multimedia Competition in the Educational and Computer Science category. The setting is a prehistoric "Flintstone" type of world, with modern conveniences. Topics covered include material from both *Primary Mathematics 1* and *2*. Each grade level has two games and several learning areas to explore.

Primary Mathematics 2A		*Rainbow Rock Primary Two*
Unit 1 – Numbers to 1000	Part 3 – Hundreds, Tens and Ones	Hundreds, Tens and Ones: Learn and Explore, Activity
Unit 2 – Addition and Subtraction	Part 1 – Meanings of Addition and Subtraction	Word Problems: Learn and Explore 1. Learn and Explore 2
	Part 5 – Subtraction with Renaming	Hundreds, Tens and Ones: Challenge 1, Game 1, Levels 1-4
Unit 5 – Multiplication and Division	Part 1 – Multiplication	Multiplication: Learn and Explore, Activity
	Part 2 – Division	Division: Learn and Explore 1. Learn and Explore 2, Activity

Unit 1 – Numbers to 1000

Objectives

- Read and write numbers less than 1000.
- Relate each digit in a 3-digit number to its place value.
- Compare and order numbers within 1000.

Suggested number of sessions: 10

	Objectives	Textbook	Workbook	Activities
Part 1 : Looking Back				**3 sessions**
1	▪ Relate 2-digit numbers to tens and ones.			1.1a
2	▪ Read and write 2-digit numbers and corresponding number-words.	p. 6 pp. 7-8, tasks 1-3	Ex. 1	1.1b
3	▪ Count on by 1, 2, 10 or 20 to a number less than 100. ▪ Count back by 1, 2, 10 or 20 from a number less than 100.	p. 9, tasks 4-6	Ex. 2	1.1c
Part 2 : Comparing Numbers				**2 sessions**
4	▪ Recognize and use the symbol ">" for "is greater than" and the symbol "<" for "is less than." ▪ Compare and order numbers less than 100.	p. 10 p. 11, tasks 1-3	Ex. 3	1.2a
5	▪ Practice.	p. 12, Practice 1A		1.2b
Part 3 : Hundreds, Tens, and Ones				**5 sessions**
6	▪ Understand the hundreds place.	pp. 13-15		1.3a
7	▪ Relate 2-digit numbers to hundreds, tens, and ones.	pp. 15-16, tasks 1-3	Ex. 4	1.3b
8	▪ Relate hundreds, tens, and ones to currency bills. ▪ Relate 3-digit numbers to number discs.	pp. 17-19, tasks 4-8	Ex. 5	1.3c
9	▪ Read and write 3-digit numbers and corresponding number-words. ▪ Compare and order numbers less than 1000.	p. 21, Practice 1B, #1-5	Ex. 6	1.3d
10	▪ Count up by 1's, 10's, or 100's. ▪ Count back by 1's, 10's, or 100's. ▪ Evaluate number patterns.	p. 20, tasks 9-10 p. 21, Practice 1B, #6-8	Ex. 7	1.3e

Part 1: Looking Back	3 sessions

Objectives

- Relate 2-digit numbers to tens and ones.
- Read and write 2-digit numbers and corresponding number-words.

Materials

- Counters or other objects that can be displayed
- Objects that students can group into tens. e.g.:
  - Counting sticks and rubber bands
  - Craft sticks and rubber bands
  - Drinking straws and tape
- Number cubes, two per group, one labeled 0-5 and the other 4-9
- Hundreds board that can be displayed
- Base-10 blocks that can be displayed

Homework

- Workbook Exercise 1
- Workbook Exercise 2

Notes

In *Primary Mathematics 1*, students learned to relate 2-digit numbers to the place value concept. The place value concept for 2-digit numbers is reviewed and reinforced in this section.

Students need to achieve a thorough understanding of place values. They should understand 2-digit numbers in terms of the part-whole model as well as in terms of tens and ones in a place-value chart. Give them adequate experience grouping concrete objects into tens and ones before using base-10 models such as base-10 blocks, money, or number discs.

A place-value chart is a table divided into columns or adjacent "places" for ones, tens, and hundreds. More columns can be added on the left side for higher place values. Each number can be written in the correct column according to its place: 136 = 1 hundred 3 tens 6 ones. In *Primary Mathematics 1*, students saw place-value charts with two columns or places for tens and ones. Now, we add a hundreds column to the place-value chart.

Hundreds	Tens	Ones
1	3	6

Base-10 materials, such as base-10 blocks, can be placed in the appropriate columns to illustrate the number. Unit-cubes go in the "Ones" column, ten-rods in the "Tens" column, and hundred-flats in the "Hundreds" column.

The number 136 is represented by 1 hundred-flat in the "Hundreds" place or column, 3 ten-rods in the "Tens" place, and 6 unit-cubes in the "Ones" place. Base-10 blocks are a concrete representation of numbers since the student can see that a ten-rod is made up of ten ones.

Hundreds	Tens	Ones
1	3	6

In part 3 of this unit, students will learn to use number discs to represent numbers. These are round discs with 1, 10, or 100 written on them. Number discs are a more abstract representation of numbers, since students do not see ten ones in a 10-disc, but they are easier to work with, since it is so easy to group and count them.

The highest number in base-10 that can go in a "place" is 9. If there are more than 10 ones in the "Tens" column, as would happen if we were to add 9 ones to 64, ten of them must be "changed" for a ten and the ten is placed in the tens column or box in order to represent the quantity numerically.

Hundreds	Tens	Ones

This guide uses the term "renamed" for the process of changing tens ones into a ten, or a ten into ten ones. For example: 4 ones + 9 ones = 13 ones. 13 ones are *renamed* as 1 ten and 3 ones. Renaming the 13 ones as 1 ten and 3 ones is equivalent to concretely replacing ten ones with a ten on the place value chart.

In the next unit, students will learn to write addition and subtraction problems in a vertical format, where the digits are aligned in columns, similar to the columns on the place-value chart, so that the "places" are next to each other in the number. The tens place is in the column next to the column for the ones place.

$$\begin{array}{r} 2\,2\,5 \\ +\ 3\,6\,2 \\ \hline 5\,8\,7 \end{array}$$

A place-value chart can have a horizontal line on it to separate the base-10 materials into two rows, one for each of the numbers being added together. When students are instructed to place or write the "3" in the ones place in a written column, they can imagine a place value chart with the "Ones" in the right-most column and write the 3 in under the right-most column of digits. Being able to align numbers carefully is an important habit for students to develop. If they have trouble aligning the digits into columns, they can be told to turn lined paper sideways, or to use graph paper.

Hundreds	Tens	Ones
2	2	5
3	6	2
5	8	7

Activity 1.1a   **Tens and ones**

1. Relate 2-digit numbers to tens and ones using concrete objects.
   - Display counters or other objects. Use a quantity greater than 20 and less than 50, such as 43. Ask students for ideas on how to count the objects. Remind them that they can count by making groups of ten.
   - Group the objects into tens with a remainder. Ask students for the number of objects.
   - Write the number as a number bond, in a place-value chart, and in tens and ones.
   - Write the number (43).

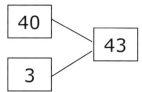

Tens	Ones
4	3

4 tens 3 ones

43

   - o Explain that this number means that we have 43 of whatever we are counting. It is made up of two digits (point to the digits). The digit in this *place* (pointing) tells us how many groups of ten. The digit in this *place* (pointing) tells us how many ones.
   - o Tell students that by having different places to put the digits, we can write large numbers without having to have a different digit for each count.
   - o Ask students how many digits we have. (10 digits, 0 to 9). We can use only those ten digits to write down any number of objects. You may want to have students name any large number they may have heard as you write the numerals.
   - Refer back to the number 43. Ask students to interpret the number in various ways by asking them questions such as the following. Refer to the place-value chart representation of the number, pointing to the digits, as students answer:

Tens	Ones
4	3

   - o 43 is 4 tens and _____ ones.
   - o 43 is _____ and 3.
   - o 43 is 3 more than _____.
   - o 3 more than 40 is _____.
   - o 40 + 3 = _____.

2. Estimate quantities less than 100 and count by grouping into tens.
   - Divide the student into groups. Give each group a number of straws and tape (or craft sticks and rubber bands).
   - Have students guess how many items they have.
   - Have them then count by grouping the number of items into tens. Assist them in bundling their groups of ten.
   - Have students record their results as tens and ones.
   - Repeat until each group has at least 9 tens bundled up.
   - Save the groups of tens for later activities.

Activity 1.1b   **Tens and ones; number-words**

1. Review tens and ones.
   - Discuss **textbook p. 6 and tasks 1-3, textbook pp. 6-8**.
     - For each task, write the number from these tasks on the board as you discuss the task. Emphasize that ones are grouped into tens, and that the number of tens is in the tens place (pointing to digit in the tens place) while the number of ones is in the ones place (pointing to the digit in the ones place).
     - In task 2, do not dwell on the number 100. That will be discussed again in part 3 of this unit. Just tell them that "100" means "one-hundred" which is the same as ten tens.
     - For task 3, you can ask questions similar to those in task 2. For example, ask students, "What is 6 more than 2 tens?" or "Forty three is 3 ones and how many tens?"

2. Discuss number-words.
   - Point to a number written on the board and tell students that the number is written in numerals, or digits. Remind them we can also write numbers out as number-words. You may want to discuss times when we write number-words, such as in writing checks. If we write out the number in words as well as write the number in numerals, there will be no mistaking what the number is, such as when someone writes too fast and their 4 might look like a 9.
   - Refer to the number-words on pages 6 and 8 of the textbook and have students read them aloud. Point out that a little line (a dash) is written between the word for the tens and the word for the ones for numbers greater than twenty.
   - Write number-words on the board. Have students copy them:
        one, two, three, four, five, six, seven, eight, nine, ten eleven, twelve, thirteen, fourteen, fifteen, sixteen, seventeen, eighteen, nineteen, twenty, thirty, forty, fifty, sixty, seventy, eighty, ninety
   - Dictate some 2-digit numbers. Students should write both the number and the number-word. Call on students to write the answers on the board so other students can check their work.
   - Optional practice: Divide students into groups and supply each group with two number cubes, one labeled with 0-5 and the other with 4-9. Students take turns throwing the dice and forming a 2-digit number which the other students write down, along with the corresponding number-word.

Workbook Exercise 1

Activity 1.1c   **Count on, count back**

1. Count by tens and ones.
   - Display a hundreds board.
   - Discuss the order of numbers on the chart:
     - Each number is one less than the number to the right of it.
     - Each number is one more than the number to the left of it.
     - Each number is ten more than the number above it.
     - Each number is ten less than the number below it.
   - Circle two numbers at random from the chart, e.g. 21 and 64. Have students count forwards or backwards first by tens and then by ones, as you point to the numbers:
     - 21, 31, 41, 51, 61, 62, 63, 64
     - 64, 54, 44, 34, 24, 23, 22, 21

- Face the students and make your hands into fists (or hold them out flat). Tell then that your right hand fist (which will be on their left) is tens, and your left hand fist is ones. Tell them that when you push up with the tens fist, they should count up by ten, when you push down with the tens fist they should count down by ten, when you push up with the ones fist they should count up by ones, and when you push down with the ones fist they should count down by one. Start at a random number and count with them as you move your fists. Be dramatic to distinguish between pushing with the fist versus returning it to its resting spot at about chest level.

2. Discuss adding 1, 2, 10, or 20 to a 2-digit number or subtracting 1, 2, 10, or 20 from a 2-digit number.
   - Refer to **task 4, textbook p. 9**. Write 65 on the board in a place-value chart. Draw a second row on the chart where you can write the answers and compare the digits just below it. As students answer the questions for task 4, ask them whether you need to change the tens or the ones. Write the corresponding equations on the board.

Tens	Ones
6	5
6	6

   - Have students do **task 5, textbook p. 9**.

$$65 + 1 = 66$$

   - Do some other examples where there is no renaming. You can include 3 and 30 more or less than a number.
   - Discuss **task 6, textbook p. 9**. To answer 80 – 1 and 80 - 2, students just count backwards by ones or tens. If there is time, you can illustrate these with a place-value charts and base-ten blocks as an introduction to renaming, which will be taught in unit 2. Put 8 tens on the chart. We can't take away a one, so we first need to rename a ten as ten ones, and then take away a ten.
   - Provide other problems where students add or subtract 1, 2, 10, or 20, writing an expression on the board and asking for the answer. Include numbers where renaming would be necessary, e.g. 29 + 2 = 31, but have students count up or back to find the answer. You can include some problems with + 3, – 3, + 30, and – 30.

Workbook Exercise 2

Part 2: Comparing Numbers   **2 sessions**

Objectives

- Recognize and use the symbol ">" for "is greater than" and the symbol "<" for "is less than."
- Compare and order numbers less than 100.

Materials

- Optional: Two cut-out cardboard pictures of crocodiles with open mouths, one facing left and one facing right, as on p. 10 of the textbook, or a 2-sided crocodile you can flip
- Base-10 blocks that can be displayed
- Number cubes, two per student or group
- Cards with 2-digit numbers, large enough for all students to see, and a symbol card with ">" on one side and "<" on the other side, or the crocodile cards

Homework

- Workbook Exercise 3

Notes

In *Primary Mathematics 1*, students learned to compare and order numbers within 100. Here, the symbols for greater than ">" and less than "<" are introduced.

By Part 2 of Unit 2, students should be able to easily recall the math facts for addition and subtraction through 20. You can have the students practice the math facts with games, activities, or worksheets. Some possible activities are given here and can be adapted for multiplication and division facts later. Other suggestions will be given throughout the guide. Spend some time each lesson reviewing the addition and subtraction facts through 20 as you do the activities in this unit and the next.

- Give students a sheet of paper with problems. Have students solve as many as they can in 5 minutes. Give them a copy of the same problems the next day and again have them see how many problems they can solve in 5 minutes. Students can see how much farther they get each day. You can do this every day or so as a warm-up exercise, using problems students need to practice. There are some mental math worksheets in this guide on the next few pages that can be used now for addition and subtraction within 20. Additional worksheets will be provided later in this guide.

- Divide the class into teams. Provide each team with a clacker or other distinctive noise maker. Hold up addition or subtraction fact cards. The team that presses the noise maker first and gives the correct answer gets a point.

- Prepare cards with answers to facts being practiced, five cards per student. Give each student five cards. Students place their cards on their desk face up. Hold up the fact cards one at a time. If a student has a card containing the answer, he or she turns the card over. The student that turns over all five cards first wins. The winner must bring the cards up to be checked with the fact cards that have been displayed.

- Use large fact cards and cards with the answers on a loop of string or masking tape folded over on the back so that the students can display their cards but leave their hands free. There should be as many fact cards and answer cards as students. Each student gets an answer card. They line up in a horseshoe shape in the numerical order of their answer cards. Stand in the opening of the horseshoe and show a fact card. Say the answer out loud and point to the student wearing the correct answer. Show another fact card. The student first pointed to must say the answer out loud and point to the student wearing the correct answer to the new fact, who is now the pointer for the next fact card. Students see how fast they can keep the game going. Once they get used to the game, they can do it silently, just pointing to the student with the answer.

- Use several sets of number cards 1-10 large enough to be seen by the whole class. Divide students into about 4 teams and line each team up. The first student in each line comes to the front of the room and draws two cards and adds the numbers on them. The student with the highest (or lowest) answer collects all the students up front to now be part of his or her team. They go back to the end of the line for their team. Play continues for a while; the team with the most members at the end wins.

- Divide students into groups. Provide each group with four sets of number cards 1-10, shuffled. The dealer deals out all cards. Each student turns over 2 cards at a time and adds the number on them. The student with the highest total gets all the cards or gets a point. Play continues until all cards are turned over. The student with the most cards or points at the end wins.

- Divide students into groups. Provide each group with four sets of number cards 1-10. One student turns over two cards. Other students must add the numbers together. The student who gets the correct answer first turns over the next two cards.

- Divide students into groups. Provide each group with four sets of number cards 1-9, shuffled, and 2 number cubes labeled with 4-9. Each group chooses a dealer who throws the number cubes and add the numbers that end up on the cubes' tops. This sum is the target number. The dealer then draws one card at a time and shows it to the other students. The students must subtract the number on the card from the target number. For example, the dealer gets 15 as the target number and draws an 8. The correct answer is 7. The student who gets the correct answer first becomes the next dealer.

Mental Math 1

1. $5 + 5 =$ _____

2. $5 + 6 =$ _____

3. $4 + 9 =$ _____

4. $9 + 4 =$ _____

5. $6 + 4 =$ _____

6. $9 + 8 =$ _____

7. $9 + 7 =$ _____

8. $7 + 5 =$ _____

9. $8 + 4 =$ _____

10. $3 + 5 =$ _____

11. $7 + 2 =$ _____

12. $9 + 6 =$ _____

13. $3 + 8 =$ _____

14. $6 + 8 =$ _____

15. $7 + 4 =$ _____

16. $2 + 2 =$ _____

17. $9 + 2 =$ _____

18. $4 + 4 =$ _____

19. $1 + 5 =$ _____

20. $8 + 8 =$ _____

21. $6 + 1 =$ _____

22. $9 + 9 =$ _____

23. $6 + 7 =$ _____

24. $3 + 2 =$ _____

25. $8 + 7 =$ _____

26. $2 + 8 =$ _____

27. $7 + 9 =$ _____

28. $6 + 6 =$ _____

29. $8 + 4 =$ _____

30. $3 + 6 =$ _____

31. $9 + 5 =$ _____

32. $3 + 7 =$ _____

33. $5 + 4 =$ _____

34. $3 + 4 =$ _____

Mental Math 2

1. $6 - 2 =$ _____

2. $6 - 4 =$ _____

3. $10 - 8 =$ _____

4. $10 - 5 =$ _____

5. $9 - 7 =$ _____

6. $10 - 7 =$ _____

7. $7 - 4 =$ _____

8. $8 - 6 =$ _____

9. $7 - 5 =$ _____

10. $7 - 2 =$ _____

11. $9 - 5 =$ _____

12. $4 - 2 =$ _____

13. $8 - 3 =$ _____

14. $10 - 3 =$ _____

15. $8 - 2 =$ _____

16. $5 - 3 =$ _____

17. $9 - 3 =$ _____

18. $10 - 9 =$ _____

19. $4 - 3 =$ _____

20. $6 - 3 =$ _____

21. $5 - 2 =$ _____

22. $7 - 6 =$ _____

23. $8 - 7 =$ _____

24. $10 - 6 =$ _____

25. $8 - 5 =$ _____

26. $9 - 6 =$ _____

27. $7 - 3 =$ _____

28. $9 - 4 =$ _____

29. $10 - 2 =$ _____

30. $8 - 4 =$ _____

31. $6 - 4 =$ _____

32. $10 - 4 =$ _____

33. $9 - 2 =$ _____

34. $6 - 5 =$ _____

Mental Math 3

1. $13 - 9 = $ _____

2. $12 - 8 = $ _____

3. $15 - 8 = $ _____

4. $12 - 4 = $ _____

5. $11 - 9 = $ _____

6. $12 - 5 = $ _____

7. $17 - 8 = $ _____

8. $11 - 5 = $ _____

9. $15 - 9 = $ _____

10. $14 - 5 = $ _____

11. $16 - 7 = $ _____

12. $14 - 8 = $ _____

13. $11 - 8 = $ _____

14. $13 - 5 = $ _____

15. $16 - 9 = $ _____

16. $12 - 9 = $ _____

17. $13 - 7 = $ _____

18. $12 - 7 = $ _____

19. $14 - 9 = $ _____

20. $13 - 8 = $ _____

21. $15 - 7 = $ _____

22. $12 - 6 = $ _____

23. $18 - 9 = $ _____

24. $11 - 7 = $ _____

25. $12 - 3 = $ _____

26. $17 - 9 = $ _____

27. $15 - 6 = $ _____

28. $14 - 7 = $ _____

29. $13 - 4 = $ _____

30. $16 - 8 = $ _____

31. $11 - 6 = $ _____

32. $14 - 6 = $ _____

33. $11 - 4 = $ _____

34. $13 - 6 = $ _____

Activity 1.2a   **Compare and order 2-digit numbers**

1. Discuss the symbols for "greater than" and "less than".
   - Ask students what sign we use to show that two numbers are equal (=). Tell them that we can also use signs to show that one number is greater than or less than another number.
   - Discuss the pictures on **textbook p. 10**. The symbol ">" and "<" can be remembered by associating them with the mouth of a greedy crocodile that eats the greater amount. If you have cardboard crocodiles, you can write two numbers on the board and have students tell you which way the crocodile must face, then trace the symbol within the mouth of the crocodile, and then remove the crocodile, leaving the symbol between the numbers. If students have trouble deciding which number is larger, illustrate them with base-10 blocks.

2. Compare and order numbers within 100.
   - Write two numbers with different tens, one above the other, with the digits aligned.
   - Point out that when we compare 2-digit numbers, we first compare the tens. The greater number has the most tens. Illustrate with base-10 blocks, if necessary. Now write the numbers next to each other, with greater than and less than symbols.
   - Write two numbers with the same digit for tens. Ask your students to compare them. Point out that if both numbers have the same tens, we then compare the ones. 38 has the same number of tens as 32, but it has more ones and so is the larger number. Illustrate with base-10 blocks, or the bundles of tens and ones students made in Activity 1.1b, if necessary.
   - Write two numbers where one is less than 10 but the ones digit is numerically larger than the tens digit in the other number. Ask students which is larger. Write one above the other, with the digits aligned. A number without any tens is smaller than a number with tens. When comparing numbers, we can't just look at the first digit of both numbers and compare them; we also need to pay attention to whether the digit is in the same place, the tens place or the ones place. You can write a 0 in the tens place of the 1-digit number to show that there are no tens.

   3 2
   5 2

   52 > 32
   32 < 52

   32 < 38

   3 2
   3 8

   12 > 9

   1 2
   0 9

   - Discuss **text p. 11, learning tasks 1-3**. Have students write the numbers in task 1 with the appropriate sign between them.

   - Write 4-5 numbers within 100 on the board and have students put them in order from smallest to greatest or greatest to smallest. Include 1-digit numbers.

Workbook Exercise 3

Activity 1.2b   **Practice**

1. Have students do **Practice 1A, Textbook p. 12**. Discuss their answers.

2. Optional games for reinforcement: compare and order 2-digit numbers.

   Game – Highest Number

   - Divide students into groups. Give each group a number cube.
   - Draw a place-value chart on the board, like the one in Activity 1.1c. Give each student some graph paper and have them draw this place-value chart, marked for ones and tens.
   - Each student rolls the number cube once, decides whether the number thrown should be a ten or a one and writes it in the appropriate place. Then each student rolls the number cube a second time and writes the number in the remaining place. The student with the highest 2-digit number at the end of a round gets a point.
   - Students also record all of their group's numbers in order for each round.

   Game – Crocodile Game

   - Use the 2-digit number cards and the crocodile card described in the material list for this section.
   - Mix cards and hold them or place the cards face-down so students do not see the numbers on the card until they get them.
   - Call three students up front. Students can come up in order of desk arrangement. Give two students numbers. Give the third student the symbol (crocodile card) card. The third student is the crocodile and must stand between the two students with the open mouth of the crocodile directed toward the student with the larger 2-digit number. That student is "eaten" and must sit down.
   - A new student comes up and gets the symbol card, while the student who originally had the symbol card gets a number card. Play continues until all students have been the crocodile.

| **Part 3: Hundreds, Tens and Ones** | **5 sessions** |

Objectives

- Relate 3-digit numbers to hundreds, tens, and ones.
- Read and write 3-digit numbers and corresponding number-words.
- Relate hundreds, tens, and ones to currency bills and number discs.
- Rename a ten as 10 ones or 10 ones as a ten.
- Rename a hundred as 10 tens or 10 tens as a hundred.
- Compare and order numbers within 1000.
- Count up from a number within 1000 by 1's, 10's, or 100's.
- Count back from a number within 1000 by 1's, 10's, or 100's.

Materials

- Overhead base-10 blocks
- Base-10 blocks for students
- Place-value charts for students
- Objects that students can group into hundreds and tens, such as straws and tape.
- Number discs for each student or group (counters labeled with 1, 10, or 100)
- Number discs that can be displayed
- Number cards 0-9, four sets for each group of students
- Number cubes, two for each student or group of students
- Some 3-digit numbers written in large numerals on cards

Homework

- Workbook Exercise 4
- Workbook Exercise 5
- Workbook Exercise 6

Notes

The concept of place value is extended to hundreds in this section. Students should have a good knowledge of place value for addition and subtraction with renaming, which will be introduced in the next unit.

Number discs are a useful alternative to base-10 blocks, since they represent a more abstract representation of place value. They are easier to group and to count and students must come to understand that ten 1-discs are the same as one 10-disc. The text makes extensive use of number discs to illustrate concepts involving the base-10 number system. You can have students label counters as number discs for use in this and succeeding lessons. The reverse sides can be used as regular counters. Students can also draw circles on an erasable place-value chart. You can label transparent counters for use with an overhead projector, or cut out cardboard discs and place magnets on the back if you have a magnetized board. You can also simply draw the discs on the board.

Activity 1.3a   **The hundreds place**

1. Introduce the hundreds place.

    *   Draw a place-value chart with three columns, with the *Ones* and *Tens* columns labeled. Use overhead base-10 blocks or other base-10 material.
    *   Students count as you place ones in the ones place. Write the number below the ones column on the chart. When you get to 9, remind them that only nine ones can go in the ones place.

	Tens	Ones
		1

    *   Ask what must be done to add another one. Ten ones must be traded in for a ten and the ten placed in the tens column on the chart. Write 1 under the tens column on the chart and 0 under the ones column. Explain that the "0" is a place-holder for tens and shows that you now have a ten.
    *   Now add more tens, one at a time, to the tens place while students count by tens. Write the number of tens below the column each time. When you get to 90, remind them that only 9 tens can go in the tens place. Ask students what we must do to add another ten.

	Tens	Ones
	1	0

    *   To add another ten, we need to have another place. Tell them that this one is called the hundreds place. Write in "Hundreds" in the left column on the chart. Trade the 9 tens plus 1 more for a hundred flat and place that in the hundreds place. Write the number 100, with the digits under the appropriate columns of the chart. Point out that both the 0's are place-holders, showing that you have 1 hundred (and zero tens, and zero ones).

Hundreds	Tens	Ones
1	0	0

    *   Now continue adding hundreds to the chart until there are 9 hundreds. Have the students count by hundreds as you do it. Tell them that the next place is the thousands place. Show them a thousand cube. Ask them how many hundreds are in the thousands cube. (10) How many tens are in the thousands cube? (100) How many ones are in the thousands cube? (1000)

2. Discuss the contents in the **textbook, pp. 13-15**.
    *   Ask students how they would count a large number of items, like a pile of straws. They could first make bundles of ten, and then put ten bundles of tens into bundles of 100. After they have one bundles of 100 straws, they can go on making bundles of tens until they either have another 100, or they have less than ten straws left.
    *   Point out that the boy on p. 13 found he did not have any left over after making four 100-bundles. So he can count by hundreds to find that he has 400 straws. Write his number of straws on a place-value chart on the board. Point out that the two 0's in the tens and ones place show that he did not have any tens or ones. If we did not write 0's in these places, we would not know whether the 4 meant 4 hundreds, 4 tens, or 4 ones. Writing the 0's puts the 4 in the hundreds columns.

Hundreds	Tens	Ones
4	0	0

    *   The boy at the top of p. 14 had one bundle of 100, no tens, and 6 straws. So he counts first the 100 bundle, then the individual straws. Write his number of straws in a place-value chart. Point out that the 0 in the tens place holds the place, so that the 1 is in the hundreds place and we know that it stands for one hundred.

Hundreds	Tens	Ones
1	0	6

    *   Discuss the other two numbers on p. 14 in a similar manner, writing the numbers in a place-value chart on the board.
    *   The top of p. 15 shows that ten bundles of 100 straws are 1000 straws.

3. If time permits, now or in the next lesson, you can do the activity illustrated on these pages. To save time, you could do it as a class activity as follows:
    *   Show the students a large pile of straws (with no more than 999 straws). Have each student guess how many they think there are and write down the numbers.
    *   Give students or groups of students each some of the straws and have them bundle them into tens. Then they need to get together to bundle their tens into hundreds until all the straws have been bundled that can be. Then have students count the bundles of hundreds, tens, and any remaining ones to find the exact number of straws.

Activity 1.3b   **Hundreds, tens, and ones**

1. Relate a 3-digit number to hundreds, tens, and ones.
    *   Discuss **task 1, textbook p. 15**.
        o   Display the number given in this task with a part-whole number bond model.
        o   Then, write the number in a place-value chart.
        o   Emphasize that in a 3-digit number, the first digit tells us how many hundreds there are, the second tells us how many tens there are, and the third tells us how many ones there are, just as if they were written in a place-value chart.

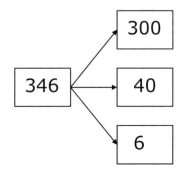

- Place some base-10 blocks on the chart to represent a 3-digit number. Call on students to supply the number. Write each number as a 3-digit number, as hundreds, tens and ones, and as a sum. For example:
  - 234
  - 2 hundreds 3 tens 4 ones
  - 200 + 30 + 4

  Include numbers where there are no tens or ones, such as 309 or 450.

309	450
3 hundreds 0 tens 9 ones	4 hundreds 5 tens 0 ones
300 + 9	400 + 50

2. Have students do **tasks 2-3, textbook p. 16**.

Workbook Exercise 4

Activity 1.3c   **Number discs**

1. Relate hundreds, tens and ones and 3-digit numbers to currency bills.
   - Show students a penny [1-cent coin] and a dime [10-cent coin]. Ask them for the value of each coin. The dime has the same value as ten pennies. We can trade in 10 pennies for a dime, and we can buy something that costs ten cents with either a dime or 10 pennies.
   - Show students a dollar bill and a ten-dollar bill. Tell them that the value of the ten-dollar bill is the same as ten one-dollar bills.
   - Discuss **task 4, textbook p. 17**. Have students count the bills on this page by counting by hundreds, then by tens (if there are any), then by ones (if there are any).
   - Point out that to write the amount of money, we write the number of hundred-dollar bills in the hundreds place, the number of ten-dollar bills in the tens place, and the number of one-dollar bills in the ones place.
   - $460 means that the value of the money is the same as four hundred sixty one-dollar bills.
   - Discuss **task 5, textbook p. 18**. A thousand-dollar bill is worth the same as ten hundred-dollar bills. Ask students how many ten dollar bills they could change for a thousand-dollar bill. (100: Each of the ten hundred-dollar bills could be changed for ten ten-dollar bills, so there would be 10 x 10 = 100 ten-dollar bills.)

2. Relate hundreds, tens and ones and 3-digit numbers to number discs.
   - Hold up or draw a counter marked with 1. Tell students that this counter can stand just for the number one, or 1 "of something". Tell them that in the same way we can mark a counter or a circle with 10 to stand for ten things, as if ten ones were bundled up into it. Hold up or draw a counter marked with 10. Ask students how many 1-discs we can change for a 10-disc (10).
   - Illustrate the problem in **task 6, textbook p. 18,** with number discs on the board. Tell students we also have 100-discs to stand for a bundle of a hundreds, or ten tens, and 1000-discs to stand for a bundle of ten hundreds.
   - A 10-disc can be "renamed" or traded in ten 1-discs. It stands for the same number of objects as ten 1-discs. Likewise, a 100-disc can be "renamed" or traded in ten 10-discs, and a 1000-disc can be "renamed" or traded for ten 100-discs.
   - Have students answer tasks 6(a) and 6(b).

3. Represent 3-digit numbers with number discs on a place-value chart.
   - Provide students with place-value charts and number discs. If you are having them draw the discs, they do not have to fill in the value of each disc; a circle in the tens column means it is a 10-disc.
   - Display a place-value chart and use or draw number discs on the board for the following discussion. You can have students first find the answers using their own place-value charts. Ask questions such as the following, illustrating with the number discs. For example, in the first question, place ten 10-discs on the chart, then remind students that we only have enough digits to show 9 in this place. Trade it in for a 100-disc, and ask how many 1-discs we would need if instead we traded each 10-disc for 1-discs.
     - How many 1's are in 10 tens?   100
     - How many 1's are in 10 hundreds?   1000
     - How many 1's are in 21 tens?   210
     - How many 10's are in 210 1's?   21
     - How many 10's are in 200 1's?   20
     - How many 100's are in 200 1's?   2
     - How many 100's are in 20 10's?   2
   - Discuss **tasks 7-8, textbook p. 19** Have students write the number represented by each picture.

Workbook Exercise 5

Activity 1.3d   **Number-words; compare and order 3-digit numbers**

1. Write number-words for 3-digit numbers.
   - Write a 3-digit number in numerals and in number-words on the board. For example, write 345 and three hundred forty-five. Tell students we write the word for the number of hundreds (three), followed by the word "hundred", followed by the rest of the number written in the same way as they learned with as 2-digit numbers. [3rd edition: there is an "and" after the "hundred".]
   - Have students read the number-words on pages 13-17 in the textbook.
   - Provide each student with a place-value chart and number discs or a dry-erase marker so that they can draw discs on their chart. Call out numbers of up to 3-digits and have the students write the numbers, place the appropriate discs on the chart, and write the corresponding number-words. If time is limited, just dictate some numbers of up to 3-digits for students to write both the number and the number-word. Show them the answer on the board so they can correct their work. Include *one thousand*. You can have students write number-words along with the numbers at any time during the year for more practice.

2. Have students do **problems 1-3, Practice 1B, textbook p. 21.**

3. Compare and order 3-digit numbers.
   - You can either ask students to find the number of different 3-digit numbers that can be made from the digits 1, 2, and 3, or simply write them on the board. There are 6 numbers: 123, 132, 213, 231, 312, and 321.
   - Write the numbers one above the other, with the digits aligned. Compare the numbers, discussing which is greatest, and which is smallest, and why. Illustrate with number discs. Point out that when we compare numbers, we first compare the values in the largest place, in this case, hundreds. If the numbers in this place are equal, we then compare the values in the tens place. If those are equal, we compare the values in the ones place.

- Use two of the numbers and write their comparison using the symbols ">" or "<", e.g.: 312 < 321.
- Give your students some additional numbers to compare or order. Include comparison of a 2-digit number to a 3-digit number, e.g. 123 and 31. Make sure students realize that even though the first digit of 123 is smaller than the first digit of 31, the 123 is greater, since the first digit is in the hundreds place. You can show this by using 0 as a place holder to show that there are no hundreds (031).

4. Have students do **problems 4-5, Practice 1B, textbook p. 21.**

5. If there is time, students can play one of the following games. These games can also be played at any time during the year.

   Game 1
   - Divide students into 2-4 teams. Use 3-digit numbers written on cards, enough for each student. Include a few 2-digit numbers.
   - Give each team as many cards as students on the team. Students must line themselves up in the order of the numbers on their cards. The first team to get in the proper order wins.
   - Students may also play a variation of the crocodile game, using 3-digit numbers (see activity 1.2b).

   Game 2
   - Divide students into groups of four. Provide each group with four sets of shuffled number cards, 0-9. The dealer deals out all the cards.
   - Each player turns over 3 numbers. The first one turned over is the hundreds (there will be no hundreds if the first number is 0), the second is the tens, and the third is the ones. The player with the highest number gets a point. You may want to have each player record all the numbers in order. The player with the most points after all cards are turned over wins.

   Game 3
   - Divide students into groups. Provide each student or group with a number cube. Students draw a place-value chart or three lines on their paper at the beginning of each round: __ __ __.
   - Each player rolls the die three times. After each roll, the student must decide whether to write the number rolled in the hundreds place, the tens place, or the ones place. Once written, it must remain in that place. The player with the highest number wins the round.
   - Students may also write down all the numbers in a round in order.

Workbook Exercise 6

Activity 1.3e   **Count on, count back**

1. Count forwards and backwards by hundreds, tens, or ones.
   - Write 2 numbers on the board. Have the class count forwards or backwards from one number to the next, first by hundreds, then by tens, and then by ones. For example, if the two numbers are 248 and 572:
     o Forwards: 248, 348, 448, 548, 558, 568, 569, 570, 571, 572
     o Backwards: 572, 472, 372, 272, 262, 252, 251, 250, 249, 248
   - Repeat with two other numbers.

2. Add or subtract 1, 2, 10, 20, 100, or 200 from a 3-digit number.
   - Discuss **tasks 9-10, textbook p. 20**. You can illustrate task 9 on the board. Students need to count up or back. If you illustrate task 10, you can show renaming, but do not dwell on renaming, since that will be taught in the next unit.
   - Write some equations on the board involving adding 1, 2, 3, 10, 20, 30, 100, 200, or 300 to a 3-digit number, or subtracting from a 3-digit number. Students should find the answer by counting up or back. For example, write 392 + 20.

3. Write number patterns.
   - Write a starting number and then give students a "rule" to create a number pattern where the hundreds, tens, or ones increase or decrease by 1 or 2. Show them how to create a number pattern following the rule. For example, write 456 and the rule "+20". The number pattern is 456, 476, 496, 516, 536.
   - Give students another number and rule and have them write the next 5 numbers following the rule.
   - Write a number pattern where one of the digits increases or decreases by 1 or 2 and ask students to find the next number. For example:
     o 183, 203, 223, _____
     o 932, 832, 732, _____

4. You can have students do the mental math worksheet on the next page now or as you continue with the next unit.

Mental Math 4

1. $432 + 10 =$ _____
2. $52 + 20 =$ _____
3. $81 + 2 =$ _____
4. $14 - 10 =$ _____
5. $398 - 20 =$ _____
6. $82 - 20 =$ _____
7. $53 + 10 =$ _____
8. $142 + 200 =$ _____
9. $604 - 10 =$ _____
10. $301 - 200 =$ _____
11. $63 - 2 =$ _____
12. $298 + 100 =$ _____
13. $748 - 100 =$ _____
14. $61 - 2 =$ _____
15. $207 - 10 =$ _____
16. $631 - 200 =$ _____
17. $199 + 10 =$ _____
18. $684 - 10 =$ _____
19. $201 - 20 =$ _____
20. $791 + 20 =$ _____
21. $317 - 20 =$ _____
22. $92 + 20 =$ _____
23. $562 + 20 =$ _____
24. $82 - 2 =$ _____
25. $541 + 300 =$ _____
26. $642 - 30 =$ _____
27. $807 - 3 =$ _____
28. $625 + 3 =$ _____
29. $670 + 30 =$ _____
30. $590 - 300 =$ _____

Unit 2 – Addition and Subtraction

Objectives

- Add and subtract numbers up to 1000.
- Solve word problems involving addition and subtraction of numbers up to 1000.

Suggested number of sessions: 23

	Objectives	Textbook	Workbook	Activities
Part 1 : Meanings of Addition and Subtraction				**3 sessions**
11	• Review the part-whole concept of addition and subtraction. • Review addition and subtraction of 1-digit numbers and tens.	p. 22 p. 23-24, tasks 1-3	Ex. 8	2.1a
12	• Compare sets by subtraction. • Relate "more than" and "less than" to addition and subtraction. • Review addition and subtraction of 2-digit numbers (no renaming).	pp. 24-25, tasks 4-8	Ex. 9	2.1b
13	• Solve word problems involving mental addition and subtraction within 100.	pp. 26-27, tasks 9-12	Ex. 10	2.1c
Part 2 : Addition without Renaming				**2 sessions**
14	• Add ones, tens, or hundreds. • Add within 100, without renaming, using the formal algorithm for addition.	p. 29, tasks 1-3	Ex. 11	2.2a
15	• Add numbers within 1000 without renaming. • Solve word problems involving addition within 1000 without renaming.	p. 28 pp. 29-30, tasks 4-7	Ex.12	2.2b
Part 3 : Subtraction without Renaming				**3 sessions**
16	• Subtract ones, tens, and hundreds. • Subtract within 100, without renaming, using the formal algorithm for subtraction.	p. 32, tasks 1-3	Ex. 13	2.3a
17	• Subtract numbers within 1000 without renaming. • Solve word problems involving subtraction within 1000 without renaming.	p. 31 pp. 32-33, tasks 4-7	Ex.14	2.3b
18	• Practice.	p. 34, Practice 2A p. 35, Practice 2B		2.3c

	Objectives	Textbook	Workbook	Activities
Part 4 : Addition with Renaming				**7 sessions**
19	▪ Add ones or tens to a 3-digit number.	p. 37, task 1	Ex. 15, #1-2	2.4a
20	▪ Add numbers within 1000, with renaming in the ones.	p. 36 pp. 37-38, tasks 2-6	Ex. 15, #3 Ex. 16, #1	2.4b
21	▪ Add numbers within 1000, with renaming in the tens.	pp. 37-8, task 7-10	Ex. 16, #2	2.4c
22	▪ Practice. ▪ Solve word problems involving addition of 2-digit numbers with renaming once.	p. 41, practice 2C, #1-2, #6-10 p. 42, practice 2C, #1-4	Ex. 17	2.4d
23	▪ Add numbers within 1000 with renaming twice.	pp. 39-40, tasks 11-14 p. 41, Practice 2C, #3-5	Ex. 18, #1-2	2.4e
24	▪ Add three numbers within 1000. ▪ Solve word problems which involve addition within 1000.	p. 40, tasks 15-16 p. 41, practice 2D, 5-10	Ex. 18, #2-3	2.4f
25	▪ Practice.		Ex. 19	2.4g
Part 5 : Subtraction With Renaming				**8 sessions**
26	▪ Subtract ones or tens from a 3-digit numbers.	p. 44, task 1		2.5a
27	▪ Subtract numbers within 1000 where the tens are renamed, using the subtraction algorithm.	p. 43, pp. 44-45. task 1-6	Ex. 20, #1	2.5b
28	▪ Practice.	p. 48, Practice 4E, #1-5		2.5c
29	▪ Subtract numbers within 1000 where the hundreds are renamed.	pp. 45-46, tasks 7-10	Ex. 21, #1	2.5d
30	▪ Subtract numbers within 1000 where there is renaming twice.	pp. 46-47, tasks 11-14	Ex.22, #1	2.5e
31	▪ Solve word problems.	p. 48, Practice 2E, #6-10 p. 49, Practice 2F, #6-10	Ex. 20, #3-5 Ex. 21, #2-4	2.5f
32	▪ Practice.		Ex. 22, #2-5	2.5g
33	▪ Subtract from a 3-digit number where renaming occurs twice before ones can be subtracted.	p. 15, tasks 15-16 p. 49, Practice 2F, #1-5	Ex. 23	2.5h

Part 1: Meanings of Addition and Subtraction	**3 sessions**

Objectives

- Review the part-whole concept of addition and subtraction.
- Use addition to find a whole, and subtraction to find a part.
- Compare sets by subtraction.
- Relate "more than" and "less than" to addition and subtraction.
- Write two addition sentences and two related subtraction sentences for a given situation for numbers within 100.
- Solve word problems involving mental addition and subtraction within 100.

Material

- Base-10 blocks that can be displayed
- Base-10 blocks for students
- Counters that can be displayed
- Number discs that can be displayed (discs with 1, 10, or 100 written on them)
- Place-value chart for students
- Number discs for students (or dry-erase marker)
- Four sets of number cards 1-9 per group, or 10-sided dice with numbers 0-9, one for each group

Homework

- Workbook Exercise 8
- Workbook Exercise 9
- Workbook Exercise 10

Notes

In Primary Mathematics 1, addition and subtraction were associated with the part-whole concept of number bonds.

To find the whole when given two parts, we add.

  5 + 3 = ?

To find a missing part given the whole and one part, we subtract.

  8 - 5 = ?

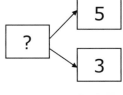

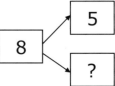

Students also learned that given a number bond, they can write a family of two addition facts and two subtraction facts:

    3 + 5 = 8   8 - 5 = 3
    5 + 3 = 8   8 - 3 = 5

These concepts are reviewed in this section. Students will also learn to compare two numbers by subtraction, and relate the terms "more than" and "less than" to addition and subtraction. For example:

> 8 is 5 more than 3
> 3 is 5 less than 8
> 3 less than 8 is 5
> Peter has 3 cars. John has 5 more cars than Peter. How many cars does John have?
> John has 8 cars. Peter has 5 fewer cars than John. How many cars does Peter have?
> John has 8 cars. Peter has 3 cars. How many more cars does John have than Peter?

In Primary Mathematics 1, students learned various strategies for adding and subtracting within 100 without the formal algorithm. These can be reviewed in this section.

➢ Add 1, 2, or 3 by counting on.
    59 + 2 = 61; count on 60, 61.

➢ Subtract 1, 2, or 3 by counting back.
    51 – 2 = 49; count back 50, 49.

➢ Add two 1-digit numbers whose sum is greater than 10 by making a 10. (This strategy is particularly useful for students who know the addition and subtraction facts through 10, but have trouble memorizing the addition and subtraction facts through 20.)

    7 + 5 = 12

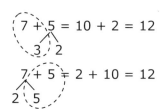

➢ Add tens to 2 digit numbers by adding the tens.

    48 + 20 = 68

➢ Subtract tens from a 2-digit numbers by subtracting the tens.

    48 – 20 = 28

➢ Add a 1-digit number to a 2-digit number by adding the ones together.

    47 + 2 = 49

➢ Add a 1-digit number to a 2-digit number where adding the ones results in a number greater than 10

    o   by making a 10, or

    o   by using basic addition facts.

    68 + 5 = 73

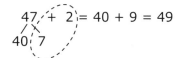

➢ Subtract a 1-digit number from a 2-digit number when there are enough ones by subtracting the ones.

   47 – 2 = 45

➢ Subtract a 1-digit number from a 2-digit number when there are not enough ones

   o   by subtracting from a 10, or

   o   by using basic subtraction facts.

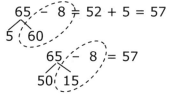

   65 – 8 = 57

➢ Add a 2-digit number to a 2-digit number by adding first the tens and then the ones.

$$+\,20 \qquad +\,5$$
$$43 \longrightarrow 63 \longrightarrow 68$$

   43 + 25 = 68

➢ Subtract a 2-digit number from a 2-digit number by subtracting first the tens and then the ones.

$$-\,30 \qquad -\,1$$
$$75 \longrightarrow 45 \longrightarrow 44$$

   75 – 31 = 44

Problems involving addition and subtraction of 2-digit numbers will not involve renaming in this part of the unit (e.g., 42 – 18 or 46 + 17).

Mental Math 5

1. $22 + 3 =$ _____

2. $52 + 5 =$ _____

3. $34 + 6 =$ _____

4. $52 + 6 =$ _____

5. $24 + 3 =$ _____

6. $25 + 5 =$ _____

7. $62 + 8 =$ _____

8. $65 + 4 =$ _____

9. $65 + 5 =$ _____

10. $65 + 6 =$ _____

11. $65 + 8 =$ _____

12. $35 + 9 =$ _____

13. $56 + 6 =$ _____

14. $57 + 6 =$ _____

15. $27 + 6 =$ _____

16. $80 + 10 =$ _____

17. $50 + 30 =$ _____

18. $38 + 3 =$ _____

19. $79 + 7 =$ _____

20. $28 + 2 =$ _____

21. $17 + 7 =$ _____

22. $19 + 8 =$ _____

23. $73 + 4 =$ _____

24. $18 + 2 =$ _____

25. $60 + 20 =$ _____

26. $36 + 3 =$ _____

27. $54 + 8 =$ _____

28. $10 + 50 =$ _____

29. $30 + 60 =$ _____

30. $93 + 7 =$ _____

Mental Math 6

1. $24 - 3 =$ _____

2. $68 - 5 =$ _____

3. $49 - 6 =$ _____

4. $59 - 3 =$ _____

5. $26 - 3 =$ _____

6. $10 - 4 =$ _____

7. $20 - 4 =$ _____

8. $70 - 4 =$ _____

9. $90 - 5 =$ _____

10. $30 - 7 =$ _____

11. $50 - 9 =$ _____

12. $51 - 9 =$ _____

13. $52 - 9 =$ _____

14. $53 - 9 =$ _____

15. $57 - 9 =$ _____

16. $80 - 7 =$ _____

17. $81 - 7 =$ _____

18. $86 - 7 =$ _____

19. $76 - 7 =$ _____

20. $28 - 2 =$ _____

21. $17 - 7 =$ _____

22. $14 - 8 =$ _____

23. $73 - 4 =$ _____

24. $16 - 2 =$ _____

25. $51 - 5 =$ _____

26. $32 - 3 =$ _____

27. $50 - 10 =$ _____

28. $80 - 50 =$ _____

29. $70 - 40 =$ _____

30. $73 - 7 =$ _____

Activity 2.1a   **Part-whole**

1. Review part-whole and number bonds.

   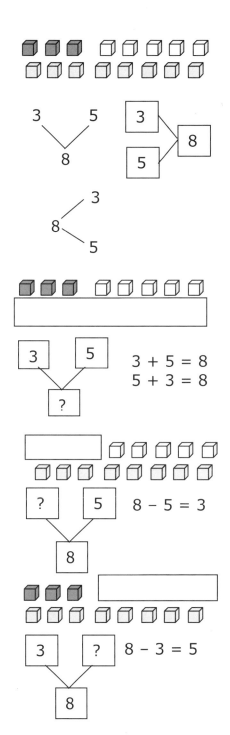

   - Display uniform-sized objects. Line some up to show two parts. Underneath them, place the same number of objects but forming a continuous line, showing the whole. You can use three different colors of objects. Explain that the top row shows two parts, and the bottom row shows the whole, i.e., the two parts together.
   - Tell students we can show the two parts and the whole with a number-bond. Draw the number bond. Tell them that the number bond does not have to be drawn with any particular orientation, as long as the lines go from the parts to the whole (or the whole to the parts). We can draw boxes around the numbers.

   - Leaving the parts, cover up or remove the whole for the objects. Draw a number bond with a question mark for the whole. Ask students how we find the whole or the total amount — we add the two parts together. Write the equation. Remind them that we can add in any order and elicit from them another equation with the addends reversed.

   - Cover up one of the parts. Tell students that we now have the total, but we are missing the part. Draw a number bond with a question mark for the missing part. Ask them how we find the missing part — we subtract. Write the corresponding equation.
   - Repeat with the other part missing. Have students supply the equation.

   - Point to, or rewrite, the first number bond and the 4 equations. Tell students that for each number bond, we can write a family of four number-sentences or equations, two addition equations and two subtraction equations. Explain that the term "equation" is used for a number-sentence where one side equals the other side.

2. Review simple word problems involving a missing whole or missing part.
   - Discuss **textbook p. 22**. Ask students what we need to find, and what information we are given to find it. We need to find the total number of cars (the whole) and are given two parts, the number of cars Ali has and the number David has. Ask them to draw a number bond with a question mark for what we need to find. Ask them how we find the total. We add the two parts.

- Discuss **task 1, textbook p. 23**. Ask students whether we are given a total and a part, or two parts. Here we are given a total (the number of cars they have altogether) and a part (the number of cars Ali has). Ask them how we find the missing part, which is the number of cars David has. We subtract.
- Discuss **tasks 2-3, textbook pp. 23-24**.
  - You can have students draw a number bond for task 2.
  - You can ask students to make up a story problem that would require one of the equations. For example, "A farmer had 12 ducklings. 5 of them were swimming on the pond, and the rest were on the land. How many were not swimming on the pond?"

3. Review addition and subtraction of ones and tens within 100. If students have not done *Primary Mathematics 1*, this may require an additional class period. Some of this review can also be done during the next two activities (2.1b and 2.1c).

- You can use base-10 blocks to illustrate and discuss addition and subtraction of 1-digit numbers or tens. Base-10 blocks allow students to see more concretely what is happening when we "make tens" or "subtract from tens". Always use the place value of the digit (i.e., "tens" and "ones") in your discussion. For example, in 50 + 40, don't say "add the 5 and the 4" but rather "add the 5 tens and the 4 tens". You may draw number bonds as well.

45 + 3 = 48
4 tens 5 ones + 3 ones = 4 tens 8 ones

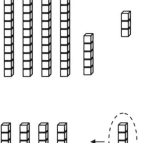

$$45 + 3 = 48$$
$$40 \quad 5$$

45 + 8 = 53
Make tens
4 tens 5 ones + 8 ones = 4 tens 5 ones + 5 ones + 3 ones
                      = 5 tens 3 ones

$$45 + 8 = 53$$
$$5 \quad 3$$

Or use addition facts
4 tens 5 ones + 8 ones = 4 tens + 13 ones
                      = 4 tens + 1 ten 3 ones
                      = 5 tens 3 ones

45 – 3 = 42
4 tens 5 ones – 3 ones = 4 tens 2 ones

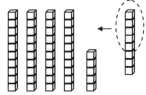

$$45 - 3 = 42$$
$$40 \quad 5$$

40 – 8 = 42
4 tens – 8 ones = 3 tens 2 ones

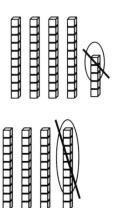

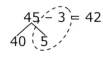

$$40 - 8 = 32$$
$$30 \quad 10$$

45 – 8 = 37
Subtract from a ten
4 tens 5 ones – 8 ones = 4 tens – 8 ones + 5 ones
                              = 3 tens 2 ones + 5 ones
                              = 3 tens 7 ones

45 – 8 = 37
5   40

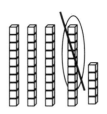

Or use subtraction facts
4 tens 5 ones – 8 ones = 3 tens 15 ones – 8 ones
                              = 3 tens 7 ones

50 + 40 = 90
5 tens + 4 tens = 9 tens

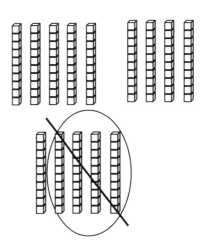

50 – 40 = 10
5 tens – 4 tens = 1 ten

- Have students do the Mental Math 5 and 6 worksheets as part of their regular fact practice.

4. Review addition and subtraction of ones and tens within 100
    Game

- Divide students up into groups of 4. Provide each group with four sets of number cards 1-9, shuffled. The dealer deals out all the cards, which the students keep, face down. For each round, each student draws 3 cards from his/her stack. The first two cards are used to create a 2-digit number. The third card is used to create a 1-digit number.
  - Game 1 – For the first two cards, the smaller one is the tens digit and the larger one is the ones digit of the 2-digit number. Each student adds their 2-digit and 1-digit numbers together and records the answer. The one with the correct smallest answer gets a point. If the answer is incorrect, the player does not get the point.
  - Game 2 – For the first two cards, the larger one is the tens digit and the smaller one is the ones digit of the 2-digit number. Each student subtracts their 1-digit number from the 2-digit number and records the answer. The student with the correct largest answer gets a point. If the answer is incorrect, the player does not get the point.
- The student with the most points when all the cards have been turned over wins.

Workbook Exercise 8

Activity 2.1b   **Comparison by subtraction**

1. Compare the quantities in two sets.
   - Display two sets of objects in two
     lines, such as yellow and red counters.

   - Ask students which set has more
     objects. How many more? Which
     has less? How many less? Show
     that we can find how many more
     or less there are in one set than
     the other using subtraction.
   - Tell students we are finding the *difference* between the numbers of objects in each set.
     The *difference* between 10 and 6 is 4. We can say this in different ways:
       o   10 is 4 more than 6
       o   6 is 4 less than 10
       o   4 less than 10 is 6 $$10 - 6 = 4$$
       o   4 more than 6 is 10
       o   The difference between 10 and 6 is 4.
   - Provide other examples

2. Have students do **tasks 4-5, textbook p. 24**.

3. Review addition and subtraction of 2-digit numbers.
   - Discuss addition of 2-digit numbers as students learned in *Primary Mathematics 1*. The
     examples should only include problems where there is no renaming. Lead them to see
     that for addition we can first add on the tens of the second number, and then the ones
     of the second number. You can use base-10 blocks or number discs to illustrate addition
     and subtraction of 2-digit numbers by first adding or subtracting the tens and then the
     ones.

     55 + 23 = 78
     55 + 23 = 55 + 20 + 3 = 75 + 3 = 78
     5 tens 5 ones + 2 tens 3 ones = 7 tens 8 ones

     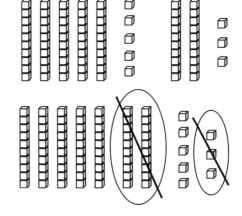

     78 – 23 = 55
     78 – 23 = 78 – 20 – 3 = 58 – 3 = 55
     7 tens 8 ones – 2 tens 3 ones = 5 tens 5 ones

     55 + 23 = 78
     23 + 55 = 78
     78 – 23 = 55
     78 – 55 = 23

   - Have the students write two addition and two
     subtraction equations.

   - Discuss some more examples. Include examples
     where two numbers are being compared. For
     example, put 78 blocks at one side and 23 at another.
     Ask:
     o   78 is how much more than 23?
     o   55 is how much less than 78?

4. Have students do **tasks 6-8, textbook p. 25**.

5. Continue to review addition of a 1-digit number to a 2-digit number and the subtraction of a 1-digit number from a 2-digit number.

Workbook Exercise 9

Activity 2.1c   **Word problems**

1. Solve word problems involving addition and subtraction of 2-digit numbers.
   - Discuss **text, pp. 26-27, tasks 9-12**. Ask the students questions to get them to think about whether we are finding a part or a whole, or whether we are comparing two numbers. Illustrate with number discs. Suggested questions are given here:
     o Task 9:   Are we given a total amount, or do we need to find a total?
                  What are the two parts?
                  The two parts are the number of key chains Danny already has, and the number he buys. We need to find a total. We add.
     o Task 10: What do we need to find? Is this a total or whole?
                  What are the two parts?
                  The two parts are the number of green apples and the number of red apples. We need to find a total. We add.
     o Task 11: Are we given a total? What is one part? What part do we have to find? How do we find how many he has left? We subtract.
     o Task 12. We are comparing two numbers. Which two? What do we need to find? How can we find how many more one number is than another? We subtract.

2. Continue to review addition and subtraction facts through 20 and mental addition and subtraction of a 1-digit numbers to or from a 2-digit number, or subtraction of 2-digit numbers when there is no renaming.

Workbook Exercise 10

Part 2: Addition without Renaming   **2 sessions**

Objectives

- Add within 1000, without renaming, using the formal algorithm for addition.
- Solve word problems involving addition within 1000, without renaming.

Materials

- Number discs (1's, 10's, 100's) that can be displayed
- Number discs (1's, 10's, 100's) for students
- Place-value charts for students
- Number cards 0-9, four sets for each group

Homework

- Workbook Exercise 11
- Workbook Exercise 12

Notes

Up to this point, students have been adding 2-digit numbers in a horizontal format using a variety of techniques, including adding the tens first and then the ones. In this section, the formal algorithm for addition is introduced for numbers of up to 3-digits.

The word algorithm originally meant the art of calculating by means of nine figures and a zero. It is used here to mean a procedure for solving a mathematical problem in a finite number of steps that frequently involves repetition of an operation. (Do not use this term with your students.)

In the formal algorithm for addition, the problem is worked in a vertical format where the digits are aligned in columns for each place. A line is drawn under the numbers to separate the sum from the numbers being added.

First the ones are added. If the sum is 10 ones or more, it is renamed as tens and ones, and the ones are written down under the line in the ones place (under the column of ones).

$$\begin{array}{r} \mathbf{1} \\ 5\ 6\ 7 \\ +\ 2\ 3\ 5 \\ \hline \mathbf{2} \\ \downarrow \end{array}$$

Then the tens are added, including any renamed ten. If the sum is 10 tens (100) or more, it is renamed as hundreds and tens, and the tens written down in the tens place under the line.

$$\begin{array}{r} \mathbf{1}\ 1 \\ 5\ 6\ 7 \\ +\ 2\ 3\ 5 \\ \hline \mathbf{0}\ 2 \\ \downarrow \end{array}$$

Hundreds are then added. This process is illustrated with number discs on p. 28 of the textbook for a situation where there is no renaming, and on p. 36 where ones are renamed.

$$\begin{array}{r} 1\ 1 \\ 5\ 6\ 7 \\ +\ 2\ 3\ 5 \\ \hline \mathbf{8}\ 0\ 2 \end{array}$$

In this section, students will be adding numbers using the formal algorithm where renaming does not occur. In part 4 they will be adding numbers where renaming does occur.

The student should have a good knowledge of place value and the basic addition facts within 20. If these facts are not yet mastered, provide opportunities to practice and master them.

In exercise 11 of the workbook, the students do not have to rewrite the problems in a vertical format. However, problems in the learning tasks in the text for this section should be rewritten in a vertical format.

As students become more proficient with adding 3-digit numbers using the vertical format, they may also become able to solve some of the problems in a horizontal format, particularly if they have a good sense of place value and can align the digits mentally. More capable students may also use an alternative algorithm or strategy where the numbers in the highest place value are added first, using mental math techniques. Do not discourage them. Flexibility with numbers indicates a good understanding of place value. However, they do need to understand the formal algorithm as taught here thoroughly, since it is the most useful algorithm for all types of problems.

Activity 2.2a   **Add hundreds and 2-digit numbers**

1. Add hundreds.
   * Provide students with place-value charts and number discs (or dry-erase markers). Have them follow the discussion by placing their own number discs on a place-value chart.
   * Display a place-value chart. Ask students: How many chairs is 5 chairs plus 2 chairs? 5 tables plus 2 tables? 5 elephants plus 2 elephants? 5 jets plus 2 jets? 5 ones plus 2 ones? 5 tens + 2 tens?

   5 ones + 2 ones = 7 ones
   5 tens + 2 tens = 7 tens
   5 hundreds + 2 hundreds = 7 hundreds

   5 + 2 = 7
   50 + 20 = 70
   500 + 200 = 700

   * Place 5 ones at the top half of the ones column on the chart, and 2 ones below it. Write the equation in terms of ones.
   * Repeat for tens and hundreds. They should think of the tens and hundreds as units. As 5 elephants + 2 elephants = 7 elephants, so do 5 hundreds + 2 hundreds = 7 hundreds. Continue with some other examples.
   * Have students do **task 1, textbook p. 29**. (These do not have to be rewritten in a vertical format.)

2. Use the formal algorithm to add 2-digits numbers, without renaming.
   * Tell students they will learn a new way for adding numbers that they can use for larger numbers. If they are good at mental math, they may not like this new method, but it is useful for adding larger numbers, or more numbers. You might want to write three 3-digit numbers, such as 398 + 476 + 258, and ask if it would be easy to add mentally. With the new way we will be learning, most of us can add these numbers together faster than if we tried to add them using the mental math strategies we have learned.
   * Write an addition equation for 2-digit numbers in vertical format. The sum of the digits in each place should be less than 10.
     o Have the students show the sum with number discs
     o Show them that when we write the numbers one below the other, we line up the ones with the ones, and the tens with the tens, just as we do in the columns on a place-value chart. You can draw a dotted line to separate the columns of digits.
     o Tell students that we can add the ones first, and then the tens. Say "4 ones plus 3 ones equal 7 ones" and write the 7 under the ones. Point out that you are writing the total number of ones in the ones place, which is under the other ones.
     o Say "2 tens plus 4 tens is 6 tens" and write 6 in the tens place. You can emphasize that the tens is written in the tens place by writing the tens and ones separately, and then writing their sum.

Hundreds	Tens	Ones
	⑩ ⑩	① ① ① ①
	⑩ ⑩ ⑩ ⑩	① ① ①

$$\begin{array}{r} 2\,4 \\ +\,4\,3 \\ \hline 6\,7 \end{array} \qquad \begin{array}{r} 2\,4 \\ +\,4\,3 \\ \hline 7 \\ 6\,0 \\ \hline 6\,7 \end{array}$$

- Have the students write the problem in the same way. Students will probably need practice in aligning the digits.
3. Have students do **tasks 2-3, textbook p. 29**.
   - They should rewrite the problems in task 3 in vertical format, aligning the digits. Tell them that they are practicing writing the numbers lined up one on top of the other so they can do it with numbers with more digits later. In their workbook exercise 11, they do not need to rewrite the problems vertically. In class, though, they should be rewriting the problems in the textbook vertically themselves, since most of the problems in the workbook, for now, are already written vertically. When they get to word problems they will have to be able to align the digits properly.

Workbook Exercise 11

Activity 2.2b   **Add 3-digit numbers**

1. Use the formal algorithm to add numbers up to 3-digits without renaming.

   - Use a place value chart and number discs to illustrate addition of a 3-digit number to a 2-digit number, and then a 3-digit number to another 3-digit number, where there is no renaming. You can use the examples in **task 4-5, textbook pp. 29-30** and on **textbook p. 28**. Do not simply discuss these problems by having the students look at the pictures in the textbook. Show each step, and relate the process on the place-value chart to the steps done with the numbers.

$$\begin{array}{r} 6\ 3\ 7 \\ +\ \ \ 2\ 2 \\ \hline 6\ 5\ 9 \end{array}$$

$$\begin{array}{r} 2\ 2\ 5 \\ +\ 3\ 6\ 2 \\ \hline 5\ 8\ 7 \end{array}$$

   - Provide some additional examples for students to solve as a class.
   - Have students do **task 6, textbook p. 30**. They should rewrite the problems in vertical format, aligning the digits. They do not have to use a place-value chart and number discs.
   - Some students may see that they can add the 3-digit numbers mentally as they did with 2-digit numbers, adding the hundreds on first, then the tens, and then the ones. They may do this in their homework.

2. Solve word problems involving addition of numbers of up to 3-digits without renaming.
   - Discuss **task 7, textbook p. 30**. Students should realize that two parts are given and the whole needs to be found, so they should add.

3. Renaming game.
   Note: Students will be learning addition with renaming later this unit. This game is meant to prepare students for renaming in addition. They can play it now or later, as time permits, before part 4 of this unit.
   - Divide students into groups. Each student needs a place-value chart and number discs (or they can write on their charts. Provide each group with four sets of number cards 0-9. The cards are shuffled and placed in the middle. Announce a target number, such as 500 or 900.
   - Players take turns drawing a card. For each number they draw, they place the same number of ones on their chart. Whenever there are 10 in the ones or tens column, they need to be traded in for a disc of the next higher place value. The first student who reaches the target number (e.g., 5 100-discs in the hundreds column) wins. If several students have reached the target number in the round, the one closest (with fewest discs in the other columns) wins.

| **Part 3: Subtraction without Renaming** | **3 sessions** |

Objectives

- Subtract within 1000, without renaming, using the formal algorithm for addition.
- Solve word problems involving addition within 1000 without renaming.

Materials

- Number discs (1's, 10's, 100's) that can be displayed
- Number discs (1's, 10's, 100's) for students
- Place-value charts for students.
- Four sets of number cards 1-9 for each group or ten-sided dice, one for each group

Homework

- Workbook Exercise 13
- Workbook Exercise 14

Notes

Up to this point, the student has been subtracting 2-digit numbers in a horizontal format using a variety of techniques, including subtracting the tens first and then the ones. In this section, the formal algorithm for subtraction is introduced.

In the formal algorithm for subtraction, the problem is worked in a vertical format.

First, the ones must be subtracted. If there are not enough ones in the top number to subtract from, a ten is renamed as 10 ones and added to the ones in the top number. There is now one less ten. The ones are subtracted and the difference written under the line in the ones place.

Then, the tens must be subtracted. If there are not enough tens in the top number to subtract from, a hundred is renamed as 10 tens and added to the tens in the top number. There is now one less hundred. The tens are subtracted and the difference written under the line in the tens place.

Then the hundreds are subtracted.

This process is illustrated with number discs on p. 31 of the text for a situation where there is no renaming, and on p. 43 where renaming occurs in the tens.

In this section, student will be subtracting numbers using the formal algorithm where renaming does not occur. In Part 5 they will be subtracting numbers where renaming does occur. Working with the number discs lets your students become comfortable with adding and subtracting larger numbers, and with renaming, so that when they come to the formal algorithm for subtraction, they will be able to appreciate it as making subtraction quicker.

Students should have a good knowledge of place value and the basic subtraction facts within 20. If these facts are not yet mastered, provide opportunities to practice and master them. As students become more proficient with subtracting 3-digit numbers using the vertical format, some may be able to solve the problems in a horizontal format, particularly if they have a good sense of place value and can align the digits mentally.

Activity 2.3a   **Subtract hundreds and 2-digit numbers**

1. Subtract hundreds.
   - Provide students place-value charts and number discs (or dry-erase markers). Have them follow the discussion by placing their own number discs on a place-value chart.
   - Display a place-value chart. Tell your students you have 7 dollars. How many would you have if you gave away 3 dollars?
   - Now ask them for the answer to 7 dogs minus 3 dogs. 7 elephants minus 3 elephants? 7 ones minus 3 ones? 7 tens minus 3 tens?
   - Place 7 on the place-value chart, and remove 3 of them. Write the equation in terms of ones. Repeat for tens and hundreds. Continue with some other examples.
   - Have students do **task 1, textbook p. 32**.

   7 ones – 3 ones = 4 ones
   7 tens – 3 tens = 4 tens
   7 hundreds – 3 hundreds = 4 hundreds

   7 – 3 = 4
   70 – 30 = 40
   700 – 300 = 700

2. Use the subtraction algorithm to subtract 2-digits numbers without renaming.
   - Tell students that we are also going to learn another way of subtracting numbers.
   - Write a subtraction equation for 2-digit numbers in vertical format (no renaming).
     - Remind students that when we write the numbers one below the other, the digits must be aligned into columns.
     - Have them place the first number of discs on their place-value chart. Say "5 ones minus 3 ones is 2 ones." Students remove the appropriate number of ones. Show them that we write the answer in the ones place under the line. Then say "6 tens minus 4 tens is 2 tens." Students remove appropriate number of tens. Show them that we write the answer in the tens place under the column of tens digits. Ask for the answer to 65 – 43.

Hundreds	Tens	Ones
	⑩ ⑩ ~~⑩~~ ~~⑩~~ ~~⑩~~ ~~⑩~~	① ① ~~①~~ ~~①~~ ~~①~~

$$\begin{array}{r} 6\,5 \\ -\ 4\,3 \\ \hline 2\,2 \end{array}$$

   - Have students write the problem down in the same way, being careful to align the digits.
   - Show students that they can check their answer by adding the number being subtracted to the answer. The number being subtracted and the answer are two parts to the whole (the number being subtracted from). 22 + 43 = 65, so 65 – 43 = 22 is correct.

3. Have students do **tasks 2-3, textbook p. 29**.
   - They should rewrite the problems in task 3 in vertical format, aligning the digits. In workbook exercise 13, they do not have to rewrite the problems and can solve them mentally.

Workbook Exercise 13

Activity 2.3b   **Subtract 3-digit numbers**

1. Use the subtraction algorithm to subtract numbers of up to 3-digits without renaming.

   - Use a place-value chart and number discs to illustrate subtraction
     of a 2-digit number from a 3-digit number, and then a 3-digit
     number from another 3-digit number, where there is no renaming.
     You can use the examples in **tasks 4-5, textbook pp. 32-33** and
     on **textbook p. 31**.
   - Provide some additional examples for students to solve as a class.

```
   6 3 7
 −   1 2
   6 2 5

   7 9 8
 − 3 6 2
   4 3 6
```

   - Have students do **task 6, textbook p. 33**. They should rewrite the problems in vertical
     format, aligning the digits.
   - Some students may see that they can subtract the 3-digit numbers mentally as they did
     with 2-digit numbers, subtracting the hundreds first, then the tens, and then the ones.
     They may do this in their homework.

2. Solve word problems involving subtraction of numbers of up to 3-digits without renaming.
   - Discuss **task 7, textbook p. 33**. Students should realize that a whole (the total number
     of people in the hall) and one part (the number of children) are given, and the other part
     (the number of adults) needs to be found, so we subtract.

3. Renaming game.
   Note: Students will be learning subtraction with renaming later in this unit. This game is
   meant to prepare students for renaming in subtraction. They can play it now or later, as
   time permits, before part 5 of this unit.
   - Divide students into groups. Each student needs a place-value chart and number discs
     (or they can write on their charts. Provide each group with four sets of number cards
     0-9. The cards are shuffled and placed in the middle. Announce a starting number
     containing 9 tens and 9 ones, such as 599 or 999.
   - Players take turns drawing a card. For each number they draw, they remove the same
     number of ones on their chart. If there are not enough ones, they must trade in a ten as
     ten ones. If there are no tens, they must first trade in a hundred as ten tens and then
     use one of those tens to trade in for ten ones. The first student who can no longer
     remove the number they draw (it is greater than their remaining ones) wins. If several
     students have reached this stage in a round, the one with the fewest ones left wins.

Workbook Exercise 14

Activity 2.3c   **Practice**

1. Practice addition and subtraction within 100 without renaming and word problems.
   - Select problems from **Practice 2A** and **Practice 2B, textbook pp. 34-35**, for students to do in class. You can work on some as a class, and have students work on others individually. You can use the remaining problems to create a worksheet for homework, or have students do them at a later time for review.
   - For the word problems, students should try to determine if a whole and part or two parts are given, or whether two quantities are being compared. If students are having difficulties, you may want set out the problem with number bonds. For example:

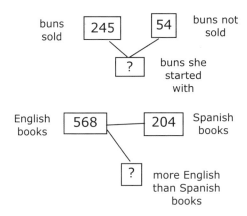

   - o #6: Write the number of buns he sold, and the number he had left. Ask students if either of them is the total. The total must be the number he sold, and the number he did not sell. Write "?" for the total and show the number bonds. Since we have two parts, and need to find the total, we add.
   - o #7: Write the number of English books, and the number of Spanish [3rd: Malay] books. Write a question mark for the number more Spanish than English books. We are comparing the number of Spanish books to the number of English books. There are more English books than Spanish books, so the number of Spanish books plus more is the number of English books. Draw lines from those two parts to the English books. We are missing a part, so we subtract

   - If students have difficulties with these problems, you can rewrite them with smaller numbers and let students act the problem out using counters to help them decide whether to add or subtract. Then do the problem again with the larger numbers.

Part 4: Addition with Renaming	7 sessions

Objectives

- Add within 1000, with renaming, using the formal algorithm for addition.
- Solve word problems involving addition within 1000 with renaming.

Materials

- Number discs (1's, 10's, 100's) that can be displayed
- Number discs (1's, 10's, 100's) for students
- Place-value charts for students
- Hundreds board that can be displayed
- Hundreds board for each student
- Number cards 1-9, four sets for each group
- Number cubes, 1-6 and 4-9, one of each per group
- Cards with addition problems (addition of two or three numbers within 1000, see activity 2.4g)
- Calendar page for each student or group

Homework

- Workbook Exercise 15
- Workbook Exercise 16
- Workbook Exercise 17
- Workbook Exercise 18
- Workbook Exercise 19

Notes

In this section, students will learn to add numbers of up to 3-digits where renaming occurs. Students will also learn to mentally add ones and tens to numbers within 1000.

All the learning task problems in the text for this unit should be rewritten vertically. Problems 1 and 2 of Exercise 15 do not have to be rewritten vertically. Students should be able to solve these by focusing on the place-value of the digit that needs to be added.

Show the students the steps, step by step, for adding with renaming using or drawing number discs on a place-value chart; don't just have them look at the pictures in the textbook, which are necessarily static showing only the final result.

More capable students may also apply other mental math techniques to the addition or subtraction of 3-digit numbers with renaming. Additional strategies will be given in *Primary Mathematics 2B* and *Primary Mathematics 3B*. Do not insist on a particular strategy when students are working individually or on their homework. Allow students to develop flexibility in working with numbers through experimenting with different ways of regrouping. They should develop their own criteria for which problems are easier to solve using the formal algorithm and which can be solved mentally or with an alternate strategy.

Mental Math 7

1. $2 + 3 =$ _____

2. $52 + 3 =$ _____

3. $452 + 3 =$ _____

4. $8 + 6 =$ _____

5. $28 + 6 =$ _____

6. $328 + 6 =$ _____

7. $2 + 8 =$ _____

8. $62 + 8 =$ _____

9. $662 + 8 =$ _____

10. $655 + 6 =$ _____

11. $659 + 8 =$ _____

12. $354 + 9 =$ _____

13. $564 + 6 =$ _____

14. $571 + 6 =$ _____

15. $277 + 6 =$ _____

16. $8 + 7 =$ _____

17. $80 + 70 =$ _____

18. $280 + 70 =$ _____

19. $283 + 70 =$ _____

20. $7 + 3 =$ _____

21. $70 + 30 =$ _____

22. $770 + 30 =$ _____

23. $777 + 30 =$ _____

24. $186 + 20 =$ _____

25. $360 + 90 =$ _____

26. $469 + 30 =$ _____

27. $469 + 3 =$ _____

28. $107 + 5 =$ _____

29. $170 + 50 =$ _____

30. $999 + 1 =$ _____

Activity 2.4a   **Add ones or tens**

1. Add ones to 3-digit numbers mentally.
   - Write the problem 7 + 5 on the board and ask students to
     solve it. Ask several students how they found the answer.
     - Make a 10: 7 + 5 = 10 + 2
     - Remember the fact 7 + 5 = 12

        $$7 + 5 = 12$$

   - Write the problem 67 + 5 on the board and ask students to
     solve it. Have some of them explain how they arrived at the
     answer. Possible methods are

        $$67 + 5 = 72$$

     - Use the answer from 7 + 5:
       If 7 + 5 is 12, then 67 + 5 = 60 + 7 + 5 = 60 + 12 = 72.
     - Make the next ten: 67 + 5 = 70 + 2 = 72
   - Write the problem 367 + 5 on the board and discuss how
     to solve it mentally.

        $$367 + 5 = 372$$
        $$300 \quad 67$$

     - Adding 5 won't affect the three hundreds. So we can
       "set aside" the 300, add 67 and 5 as before, and then
       put back in the 300. You can illustrate this with number
       bonds. You may also want to illustrate this with number
       discs.
   - Repeat with another set of examples, such as:
     - 8 + 7
     - 48 + 7
     - 648 + 7

2. Add tens to 3-digit numbers mentally.
   - Write a problem such as 6 + 7 on the board and ask
     students to solve it.

        $$6 + 7 = 13$$

   - Write 60 + 70 on the board and discuss how to solve it
     mentally. Since 6 ones + 7 ones = 13 ones, then 6 tens +
     7 tens = 13 tens. Show this on a place-value chart with
     number discs. We have to rename ten of the tens as a
     hundred, so 13 tens = 1 hundred 3 tens 0 ones = 130.

        $$60 + 70 = 130$$

   - Write 46 + 7 on the board and have students solve it.

        $$46 + 7 = 53$$

   - Write 460 + 70 on the board and discuss how to solve it.
     46 is 46 ones. If 46 ones + 7 ones = 53 ones, then 46
     tens + 7 tens = 53 tens, or 530, five hundred thirty. 50
     tens is the same as 5 hundreds.

        $$460 + 70 = 530$$

   - Write 462 + 70 on the board and discuss how to solve it.
     We are adding tens only. We can ignore the ones in 462 for
     now, add tens as with 460 + 70, and then add back in the
     ones. You can show this with number bonds.

        $$462 + 70 = 532$$
        $$2 \quad 460$$

   Have students do some other renaming problems, such as:
     - 23 tens = _____ hundreds _____ tens = 230
     - 35 tens = _____ hundreds _____ tens = _____
     - 40 tens = _____ hundreds _____ tens = _____
   - Repeat with some other examples, such as:
     - 8 + 7
     - 80 + 70
     - 48 + 7
     - 780 + 70
     - 785 + 70

3. Have students to **task 1, textbook p. 37**.

4. You can have students do the Mental Math 7 worksheet for additional practice.

   Workbook Exercise 15, #1-2

Activity 2.4b   **Add with renaming in the ones**

1. Add 2 numbers within 1000 with renaming in the ones.
   * Provide students with place-value charts and number discs.
   * Write the problem 36 + 8 on the board and have students solve it.
     o Show students the steps for solving this problem. Show each step first with number discs, and then with numbers. Begin by placing 3 tens and 6 ones onto the place-value chart. Now place 8 more ones into the ones place.
     o Rewrite the problem in vertical format. Show each step first with number discs, and then with numbers.
     o There are too many ones in the ones place. Ask students how many ones we have (14). We don't have a single digit to show 14, so we need to rename ten ones as a ten and put that in the tens column. We now have 4 tens and 4 ones.
     o We show this step on the number by writing the tens above the 3 in the tens column and the ones below the line in the ones column. This is the same as renaming 14 ones as 1 ten and 4 ones.
     o Then we add the tens (1 ten + 3 tens) to find the total tens, which we write below the lines in the tens column.

   * Write the problems 36 + 28 on the board in a vertical format. Guide students in solving this problem using the addition algorithm (shown on **textbook p. 36**). Show each step with number discs on the place-value chart, and then show how that step is recorded in the numerical representation. This is the same as the previous problem, except that we just have two more tens.
   * Repeat with 336 + 28. We add the ones and tens in the same way, but now we also have hundreds.

- Repeat with 336 + 128. We add the ones and tens in the same way, and then add the hundreds.

$$\begin{array}{r} {\scriptstyle 1} \\ 3\ 3\ 6 \\ +\ 1\ 2\ 8 \\ \hline 4\ 6\ 4 \end{array}$$

- Guide students through additional problems where they must add 2 or 3-digit numbers where the ones have to be renamed. Do some with number discs as needed, and then without. You can use the problem in **tasks 3 and 5**, and some of the problems from **tasks 2, 4, and 6, textbook pp. 37-38**

2. Have students do the rest of the problems in **tasks 2-6, textbook pp. 37-38**. Some of these problems can be used for review, later, if there is not time to complete them all in one session.

Workbook Exercise 15, #2
Workbook Exercise 16, #1

Activity 2.4c   **Add with renaming in the tens**

1. Add 2 numbers within 1000 with renaming in the tens.
   - Provide students with place-value charts and number discs.
   - Guide students through the addition algorithm for 63 + 56, 563 + 56 (**task 7, textbook p. 38**) and 563 + 356, using number discs and a place-value chart. We do not have to rename ones, but when we add the tens we get 11 tens, so we must trade in ten tens as a hundred. We show this by writing the hundred above the hundreds column and the tens below the line.
   - Provide additional examples as needed, with and then without the number discs.

$$\begin{array}{r} 6\ 3 \\ +\ \ 5\ 6 \\ \hline 1\ 1\ 9 \end{array}$$

$$\begin{array}{r} {\scriptstyle 1} \\ 5\ 6\ 3 \\ +\ \ \ 5\ 6 \\ \hline 6\ 1\ 9 \end{array}$$

$$\begin{array}{r} {\scriptstyle 1} \\ 5\ 6\ 3 \\ +\ 3\ 5\ 6 \\ \hline 9\ 1\ 9 \end{array}$$

2. Have students do **tasks 8-10, textbook pp. 38-39**.

Workbook Exercise 16, #1

Activity 2.4d   **Add with renaming once, word problems**

1. Solve word problems which involve addition with renaming once.
   - Discuss **problems 6-10, Practice 2C, textbook p. 41**. These problems all involve addition with renaming in only one place, or subtraction without renaming. Students must decide whether to add or subtract. You can guide them in determining whether the problem gives two parts and asks for a whole, or one part and a total and asks for the other part.

2. Provide additional practice in addition with renaming once.
   - You can use any problems in **tasks 1-10, textbook pp. 37-39** which students have not yet done in the previous sessions.
   - You can use **problems 1-2, Practice 2C, textbook p. 41** and **problems 1-4, Practice 2D, textbook p. 42**.

3. Optional: Have students play one of the following games.

Game – Add tens or ones

Divide the students into groups of 4. Provide each group with a number cube labeled with 1-6, or a regular die.

Roll 1: 5		5	0
Roll 2: 2		2	0
Total		7	0
Roll 3: 3			3
Total		7	3
Roll 4: 5			5
Total		7	8
Roll 5: 4			4
Total		8	2
Roll 6: 1		1	0
Total		9	2
Roll 7: 6			6
Total		9	8

- Game 1: Provide each group number discs. The players take turns rolling the number cube. After each roll, the player must decide whether to get tens or ones for the number rolled. Any time he or she has 10 ones, they must be traded in for a ten. Each player rolls 7 times. After 7 rolls, the player (in each group) with a total closest to 100 wins.
- Game 2: Play the game as in Game 1, except that the player writes the tens or the ones down on paper and adds it to the previous total without using number discs.

   Variation: Add tens, ones, or hundreds.
   Students must decide whether the number rolled is to be hundreds, tens, or ones. The goal is to be as close to 900 as possible after 7 rolls.

Game – Add 2-digit numbers

- Divide students into groups of four. Provide each group with four sets of number cards 1-9.
- In each group, the dealer shuffles the cards and turns over the first two cards. The first card is the tens and the second card is the ones. This constitutes the target number. The dealer then deals four cards to each player. The players arrange their cards into two 2-digit numbers so that their sum will be as close to the target number as possible. The winner is the player whose sum is the closest. For example, the target number is 45. A player turns over 9, 3, 5, and 1. He or she can form the two numbers 19 and 35 for a sum of 54, which is 9 more than the target number, but still closer to 54 than the sum of other possible paired numbers.

Workbook Exercise 17

Activity 2.4e   **Add with renaming twice**

1. Add numbers of up to 3-digits where renaming occurs in both the ones and the tens.
   - Provide students with place-value charts and number discs.
   - Illustrate the steps for adding a 2-digit number to a 3-digit number where there is renaming in both the tens and the ones, and then adding two 3-digit numbers using a place-value chart and number discs. Then do some examples without number discs.

$$\begin{array}{r} \overset{1\ 1}{} \\ 5\ 6\ 7 \\ +\ 5\ 6 \\ \hline 6\ 2\ 3 \end{array}$$

   - In the examples at the right, 7 ones + 6 ones = 13 ones = 1 ten 3 ones. Write this ten above the tens column and the ones under the line (in the ones column).
   1 ten + 6 tens + 5 tens = 12 tens = 1 hundred 2 tens
   Write the hundred above the hundreds column and the tens under the line (in the tens column). Add the hundreds, and write the answer below the line (in the hundreds column).

$$\begin{array}{r} \overset{1\ 1}{} \\ 5\ 6\ 7 \\ +\ 2\ 5\ 6 \\ \hline 8\ 2\ 3 \end{array}$$

2. Have students do **tasks 11-14, textbook pp. 39-40** and **problems 3-5, Practice 2C, textbook p. 41**.

   Workbook Exercise 18, #1

Activity 2.4f   **Add three numbers, word problems**

1. Add three numbers of up to 3-digits.
   * Discuss **task 15, textbook p. 40**.
   * Point out that we do not have to add the numbers in order in each column. Do another example where it helps to change the order the numbers are added in, such as 456 + 127 + 94. For the ones, if we add 6 and 4 first, we get a ten, and then we can add the 7. For the tens, we can add 9 and 1 first.

$$
\begin{array}{r}
1\ 1\ \ \\
4\ 5\ 6 \\
1\ 2\ 7 \\
+\ \ \ 9\ 4 \\
\hline
6\ 7\ 7
\end{array}
$$

2. Have students do **task 16, textbook p. 40** and **problem 5, Practice 2D, textbook p. 42**.

3. Have students do **problems 6-7, Practice 2D, textbook p. 42**, or discuss the problems as a class. You can select several to discuss as a class, and have students work on others individually. They need to decide whether to add or subtract. They can draw diagrams or number bonds.

   Workbook Exercise 18, #2-3

Activity 2.4g   **Practice**

1. Provide additional problems for students to practice adding within 1000. You may want to spend an extra session on practice or the games or investigations below.

2. Optional: Have students play one of the following games.

   Divide students into groups of four. Provide each group with four sets of number cards 1-9. Each group selects a dealer.
   Game 1 - Add 3-digit numbers
       The dealer deals 6 cards to each player. The players arrange their cards into two 3-digit numbers and add these together. The player with the <u>lowest</u> sum wins.
       After the students have played several games, discuss with the students how they formed the numbers to give the lowest sum. Then allow the students to play a few more rounds.
   Game 2 - Add 3 numbers
       The dealer deals 8 cards to each player. Each player arranges the cards into two 3-digit numbers and one 2-digit number and adds them together. The player with the *lowest* sum wins.

Game - Add 3-digit numbers (This is a long game.)

* Prepare in advance cards containing problems involving addition of 2 or 3 numbers within 1000. Have students form a line around the room.
* Show the first card. As an example, this card has 368 + 45. The first student must give the sum of the ones in terms of tens and ones (8 ones + 5 ones = 1 ten 3 ones). The second student must give the sum of the tens in terms of hundreds and tens (1 ten + 6 tens + 4 tens = 1 hundred 1 ten). The third student must give the sum of the hundred (1 hundred + 3 hundreds = 4 hundreds). The fourth student must give the answer to the problem (413). If that student has the correct answer, he or she comes up front to hold up the next card, and then sits down when the next person comes up. The fifth student starts on the next problem, adding the ones. Play continues until all or most students have sat down.

3. Optional: Have students do the following investigations.

   Investigate addition of 3-digit numbers.

   * Discuss the following or similar problems. The students can rewrite the problem in a vertical format, if necessary:
     o 2 hundreds + 4 tens + 28 ones = _____
     o 17 tens + 457 ones = _____
     o 143 more than 62 is _____
   * Discuss some problems with missing addends. For example:

$$\begin{array}{r} 2\ 4\ 9 \\ +\ 1\ \square\ 0 \\ \hline 4\ 3\ 9 \end{array} \qquad \begin{array}{r} 6\ \square\ 8 \\ +\ 1\ 3\ \square \\ \hline 7\ 6\ 3 \end{array} \qquad \begin{array}{r} 2\ 8\ 4 \\ +\ \square\ 7\ \square \\ \hline 9\ 5\ 4 \end{array}$$

   Investigate number patterns.

   * Provide each student with a hundreds board and a calendar page of the current month.
   * Display a hundreds board. Draw a box around any four numbers. Ask the students to add the numbers in each diagonal. What do they notice?
   * Draw a box around nine numbers. Have the students add the 3 numbers in each diagonal.
   * Allow the students to try with other groups of 4 or 9 numbers to see if they still get the same sum. Some students could try it with a group of 16 numbers.
   * Have them try the same thing with the numbers on a calendar.
   * Discuss why the sums of the numbers in each diagonal are the same. You can use number bonds to show that if we separate tens and ones, each diagonal has the same tens and ones (20 + 30 + 40 + 2 + 3 + 4).
   * Have students see if there are other sums in the 3 by 3 box that have the same sum as the diagonals.

37	38
47	48

37 + 48 = 85
47 + 38 = 85

22	23	24
32	33	34
42	43	44

22 + 33 + 44 = 99
42 + 33 + 24 = 99

| Part 5: Subtraction with Renaming | 8 sessions |

Objectives

*   Subtract within 1000, with renaming, using the formal algorithm for subtraction.
*   Solve word problems involving subtraction within 1000 with renaming.

Material

*   Number discs (1's, 10's, 100's) that can be displayed
*   Number discs (1's, 10's, 100's) or base-10 blocks for students
*   Place-value charts for students
*   Four sets of number cards 0-9 for each group
*   Number cubes labeled with 4-9, one for per group
*   Number cube labeled with 1-6 (or regular dice), 3 for each group

Homework

*   Workbook Exercise 20
*   Workbook Exercise 21
*   Workbook Exercise 22
*   Workbook Exercise 23
*   Workbook Exercise 24
*   Review 1

Notes

In this section, the student will learn to subtract numbers of up to 3 digits.

More capable students should be permitted to use mental shortcuts while solving the subtraction problems.

Mental Math 8

1. $11 - 3 = \underline{\hspace{2cm}}$

2. $61 - 3 = \underline{\hspace{2cm}}$

3. $961 - 3 = \underline{\hspace{2cm}}$

4. $14 - 8 = \underline{\hspace{2cm}}$

5. $64 - 8 = \underline{\hspace{2cm}}$

6. $264 - 8 = \underline{\hspace{2cm}}$

7. $146 - 4 = \underline{\hspace{2cm}}$

8. $146 - 9 = \underline{\hspace{2cm}}$

9. $909 - 5 = \underline{\hspace{2cm}}$

10. $999 - 5 = \underline{\hspace{2cm}}$

11. $990 - 5 = \underline{\hspace{2cm}}$

12. $991 - 5 = \underline{\hspace{2cm}}$

13. $452 - 9 = \underline{\hspace{2cm}}$

14. $653 - 8 = \underline{\hspace{2cm}}$

15. $357 - 2 = \underline{\hspace{2cm}}$

16. $12 - 7 = \underline{\hspace{2cm}}$

17. $120 - 70 = \underline{\hspace{2cm}}$

18. $126 - 70 = \underline{\hspace{2cm}}$

19. $62 - 7 = \underline{\hspace{2cm}}$

20. $620 - 70 = \underline{\hspace{2cm}}$

21. $628 - 70 = \underline{\hspace{2cm}}$

22. $540 - 80 = \underline{\hspace{2cm}}$

23. $549 - 80 = \underline{\hspace{2cm}}$

24. $360 - 50 = \underline{\hspace{2cm}}$

25. $330 - 50 = \underline{\hspace{2cm}}$

26. $832 - 30 = \underline{\hspace{2cm}}$

27. $500 - 60 = \underline{\hspace{2cm}}$

28. $506 - 60 = \underline{\hspace{2cm}}$

29. $516 - 60 = \underline{\hspace{2cm}}$

30. $732 - 90 = \underline{\hspace{2cm}}$

Activity 2.5a   **Subtract ones or tens**

1. Subtract ones from 3-digit numbers mentally.
   - Write the problem 12 – 7 on the board and ask students to solve it. Ask several how they found the answer. Possible methods are:
     - Subtract from the 10: $12 - 7 = 10 - 7 + 2 = 3 + 2 = 5$
     - Subtract 2, then 5 more: $12 - 7 = 12 - 2 - 5 = 10 - 5 = 5$
     - Count up from 7 to 10 first, then to 12.
     - Remember the fact $12 - 7 = 5$

   $12 - 7 = 5$

   - Write the problem 62 – 7 on the board and ask students to solve it. Have some of them explain how they arrived at the answer. Possible methods are
     - Use the answer from 12 – 7.
       If 12 – 7 is 5, then $62 - 7 = 50 + 12 - 7 = 55$.
     - Subtract 7 from 60, which is 53, then add on the 2.

   $62 - 7 = 55$
   50 12

   $62 - 7 = 55$
   2   60

   - Write the problem 362 – 7 on the board discuss how to solve it mentally.
     - Subtracting 7 won't affect the three hundreds. So we can "set aside" the 300, subtract 7 from 62 as before, and then put back in the 300. You can illustrate this with number bonds. You may also want to illustrate this with number discs.

   $362 - 7 = 355$
   300   62

   - Repeat with another set of examples, such as:
     - 15 – 9
     - 45 – 9
     - 645 – 9

2. Subtract tens from 3-digit numbers mentally.
   - Write the expression 16 – 7 on the board and ask students to solve it.

   $16 - 7 = 9$

   - Write the expression 46 – 7 on the board and ask students to solve it mentally.

   $46 - 7 = 39$

   - Write 460 – 70 on the board and discuss how to solve it mentally.
     - Since 46 ones – 7 ones = 39 ones, then 46 tens – 7 tens = 39 tens, which is 390. So we can solve this problem in the same way as we solve 46 – 7, but the answer is tens, rather than ones. You can show this with number discs, replacing one hundred with 3 tens (to show 100 – 70 = 30), which you place in the tens column, so there are now 3 hundreds and 9 tens.

   $460 - 70 = 390$

   - Write 462 – 70 on the board and discuss how to solve it. We are subtracting tens only. We can ignore the ones in 462 for now, subtract tens as with 460 – 70, and then add back in the ones. You can show this with number bonds.

   $462 - 70 = 392$
   2   460

   - Repeat with some other examples, such as:
     - 63 – 8
     - 630 - 80
     - 638 - 80

3. Have students to **task 1, textbook p. 44**.

4. You can have students do the Mental Math 8 worksheet for additional practice.

Activity 2.5b   **Subtract with renaming of tens**

1. Subtract within 1000 with renaming in the tens.
    *   Provide students with place-value charts and number discs.
    *   Tell students that we will now learn another way to solve subtraction problems when there are not enough ones to subtract.
    *   Write the problem 62 – 3 on the board in a vertical format.
    *   Show students the steps for solving this problem using the subtraction algorithm, illustrating the steps with a place-value chart and number discs.
        o   Place 6 tens and 2 ones on the chart. Tell students that there are not enough ones to take 3 away from. We can rename a ten as ten ones. Replace a 10-disc with ten 1-discs.
        o   We show this on the problem by crossing out the tens, writing one less ten above it, and putting a little one next to the 2 (or crossing it out and writing 12). We have renamed 6 tens 2 ones as 5 tens 12 ones.
        o   We now have enough ones to take away 3. Remove 3 1-discs. That leaves 9 ones.
        o   We show this on the problem by writing a 9 below the line in the ones column. We have 5 tens left, so we write that below the line in the tens column. 62 – 3 = 59.

*   Show students that they can check their answer by adding "upside down". Does 59 + 3 = 62? 3 and 9 is 12, which gives the 2 in 62, and then 5 tens and the 1 ten from 9 + 3 is 6. So the answer is correct.

*   Write the problems 62 – 43 on the board in a vertical format. Guide students in solving this problem using the subtraction algorithm (shown on **textbook p. 36**). Show each step with number discs on the place-value chart, and then show how that step is recorded on the numerical representation. This is the same as the previous problem, except that we now need to also subtract tens.

*   Repeat with 562 – 43.

*   Repeat with 562 – 243.

- Guide the students through the steps for **task 3, textbook p. 44 and task 5, textbook p. 45**. Task 3 is shown at the right.

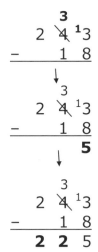

2. Have students do the rest of the problems in **tasks 2-6, textbook pp. 44-45**. Some of these problems can be used in the next session, if there is not time to complete them all in one session. Students can check their answers with addition.

Workbook Exercise 20, #1

Activity 2.5c   **Practice**

1. Have students do **Problems 1-5, Practice 2E, textbook p. 48**.
   - They can solve these mentally or using the subtraction algorithm.
   - Provide additional practice problems with 3-digit numbers with some involving renaming in the tens. Include problems where there is no renaming, so that students don't simply start crossing out tens without first seeing whether it is necessary.

2. Optional: Have student play one of the following games.

   Game - Subtract ones, tens, or hundreds.
   - Divide students up into small groups. Provide each group with one number cube labeled with the numbers 4-9.
   - Provide each group with number discs and a place-value chart. Each player starts with 9 hundreds and 5 tens. The players take turns rolling the die. After each roll, the players must decide whether the number rolled should be a hundred, a ten, or a one. They must remove the corresponding amount from the discs on the place-value chart, trading a 100-disc for ten 10-discs and/or a 10-disc for ten 1-discs. Each player rolls 7 times. If the player rolls a number that is greater than the number of ones he has left at the end, he or she loses the round. After 7 rolls, the player closest to 0 wins.
   - In the rare occasion where renaming twice might occur, such as having 101 and rolling 9 which is taken as ones, until they have done activity 2.5h (subtract when there are no tens) you can guide the student in trading in the hundred disc for ten 10-discs and then a ten disc for ten 1-discs. Students might think to do this on their own.
   - After you teach the next session (renaming hundreds) students can do this game without number discs, writing their equations down on paper.

	9	5	0
Roll 1: 4	4	0	0
Difference	5	5	0
Roll 2: 6		6	0
Difference	4	9	0
Roll 3: 4	4	0	0
Difference		9	0
Roll 4: 6		6	0
Difference		3	0
Roll 5: 9			9
Difference		2	1
Roll 6: 8			8
Difference		1	3
Roll 7: 4			4
Difference			9

Game - Subtract 2-digit numbers.

- Divide students up into groups of four. Provide each group with four sets of number cards 1-9. Each group selects a dealer.
- The dealer shuffles the cards and turns over the first two cards. The first card is the tens and the second the ones of what becomes target number.
- The dealer then deals four cards to each player. The players arrange their cards into two 2-digit numbers so that the difference will be as close to the target number as possible. The winner in each group is the player whose answer is the closest to the target number. For example, the target number is 45. A player turns over 9, 3, 5, 1. He can form the two numbers 93 and 51 and subtract them to get 42, which is 3 less than the target number.

Activity 2.5d   **Subtract with renaming of hundreds**

1. Subtract within 1000 with renaming in the hundreds.
   - Discuss **task 7, textbook p. 45** (729 – 64). Illustrate the steps with number discs on the board.
     - First we subtract the ones. 9 ones – 4 ones = 5 ones. We write the ones under the line (in the ones column).

     - Then we subtract the tens. There are not enough tens. So we have to rename a hundred as 10 tens. We will have one less hundred. We show this by crossing out the 7 hundreds and writing a 6 above it in the hundreds place to show that we have 6 hundreds now. We can write a little 1 next to the 2 in the tens place to show that we now have 12 tens.

     - Now we have enough tens, and can subtract 6 tens. We are left with 6 tens. We write 6 under the line (in the tens column) to show that we have 6 tens.

     - We are left with 6 hundreds, so we write 6 under the line (in the hundreds column).

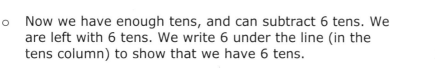

$$
\begin{array}{r}
7\ \ 2\ \ 9 \\
-\ \ \ \ 6\ \ 4 \\
\hline
\mathbf{5}
\end{array}
$$

$$
\begin{array}{r}
{}^{6}\!\!\!\not{7}\ \ {}^{1}2\ \ 9 \\
-\ \ \ \ 6\ \ 4 \\
\hline
\mathbf{6}\ \ 5
\end{array}
$$

$$
\begin{array}{r}
{}^{6}\!\!\!\not{7}\ \ {}^{1}2\ \ 9 \\
-\ \ \ \ 6\ \ 4 \\
\hline
\mathbf{6}\ \ 6\ \ 5
\end{array}
$$

- Similarly, discuss **task 9, textbook p. 46** (538 – 293). Illustrate the steps with number discs.

2. Have students do **task 8, textbook p. 45** and **task 10, textbook p. 46**.

Workbook Exercise 21, #1

Activity 2.5e   **Subtract with renaming twice**

1. Subtract within 1000 where both tens and hundreds must be renamed.
   - Provide students with place-value charts and number discs.
   - Guide students through the problems in **task 11, textbook p. 46** and **task 13, textbook p. 47**, illustrating each with number discs. In both tasks, there are not enough ones, so a ten has to be renamed as 10 ones. Then, there are not enough tens to subtract from, so a hundred has to be renamed as 10 tens.
   - Illustrate a few more problems where renaming occurs twice.

2. Have students do **tasks 12 and 14, textbook p. 47**.
   - Provide additional problems as needed.

Workbook Exercise 22, #1

Activity 2.5f   **Word problems**

1. Solve word problems involving subtraction of 2-digit numbers.
   - Discuss some of the word problems in **Practice 2E, textbook p. 48** and **Practice 2F, textbook p. 49** as a class and have students do some of them individually and share their solutions.
   - The students should determine whether a comparison is being made, or what information provides the whole and what provides the part. (Problems 6 and 10 on p. 48 and problems 7 and 10(b) on p. 49 involve addition. The rest involve subtraction)
   - You may want to show diagrams or number bonds to help students see how to solve these problems. Students can draw number bonds.
   - For example:
     - Jenny collected 92 shells. Write 92 to show how many she collected. This is 9 more than Mary collected. We don't know how many Mary collected, so we can draw a circle with a "?" in it. We are told that Jenny collected 9 more than Mary. So we are comparing the number of Jenny's shells to the number of Mary's shells. Who has more? Jenny does. So to find how many shells Mary has, we need to take 9 away from the number of shells that Jenny has.

     92
     / \
    ?   9

     ? = 92 – 9 = 83

   - If students find any of these problems difficult, rephrase them with smaller numbers where they can act out the problems with counters.

Workbook Exercise 20, #3-5
Workbook Exercise 21, #2-4

Activity 2.5g   **Practice**

1. Provide students with problems so that they can practice subtraction within 1000.

2. Have students play one of the following games.

   Divide students up into groups of four. Provide each group with four sets of number cards 1-9. Each group selects a dealer.

   Game1:
   The dealer shuffles the cards and turns over the first three cards. The first card is the hundreds, the second card the tens and the third card the ones of what becomes the target number. The dealer then deals six cards to each player. The players arrange their cards in to two 3-digit numbers so that the difference will be as close to the target number as possible. The winner is the player whose difference is the closest.
   Game 2:
   The dealer deals 6 cards to each player. The players arrange their cards into two 3-digit numbers and subtract. The player with the *lowest* difference wins.

Workbook Exercise 22, #2-5

Activity 2.5h   **Subtract when there are no tens**

1. Subtract from a 3 digit number when both hundreds and ones need to be renamed. Spend time on this skill, with plenty of examples and more practice than just the 4 problems in the textbook, since some students will continue to have trouble knowing what to do when they cannot rename the next higher place value.

   - Provide students with place-value charts and number discs.
   - Discuss the problem in **task 15, textbook p. 47**, using number discs to show each step. Write the on the board and ask for suggestions on how to solve this problem from the students. What should be done if we don't have enough ones, and there are not any tens to rename? We can rename a hundred as 10 tens, and then one of those tens as 10 ones. Point out that we are renaming the hundred as 9 tens and 10 ones.
   - Illustrate a few more similar problems.

2. Have students do **task 16, textbook p. 47** and **problems 1-5, Practice 2F, textbook p. 49**.

3. You can have students play one of the games in activity 2.5g, but include two 0's in each set of number cards 1-9.

Workbook Exercise 23

Review 1

Objectives

- Add and subtract numbers up to 1000.
- Solve word problems involving addition and subtraction of numbers up to 1000.

Suggested number of sessions: 2

	Objectives	Textbook	Workbook	Activities
34 35	▪ Review	p. 50, Practice 2G p. 51, Practice 2H	Ex. 24 Review 1	R.1

Activity R.1   **Review**

1. Use the problems in **Practice 2G, textbook p. 50** and **Practice 2H, textbook p. 51** to review addition and subtraction within 1000. Allow students to choose whether to solve the problems mentally or by using the algorithm. You can call on students to explain their solutions to the word problems. You may also wish to review topics from unit 1 (see review 1 in the workbook).

2. Optional: Game

   Divide the students up into small groups. Provide each group with 3 number cubes or dice.

   Each player rolls the 3 number cubes twice, writing down the numbers they get. On the first roll, they make the largest 3-digit number possible, and on the second roll the make the smallest 3-digit number possible. They then subtract the two numbers. The answer is the score for that round. After each round, the score is added to the previous total. The first person to reach 750 wins.

3. Optional: Investigations

   - Discuss the following or similar problems:
     ➤ 457 is 42 more than _____
     ➤ _____ is 35 more than 901
     ➤ 856 − 450 = 100 + _____

   - Discuss some problems with missing digits. For example:

$$
\begin{array}{r}
3\ 0\ 2 \\
-\ 1\ \square\ 8 \\
\hline
\square\ 3\ 4
\end{array}
\qquad
\begin{array}{r}
4\ \square\ 2 \\
-\ 3\ 1\ \square \\
\hline
1\ 3\ 4
\end{array}
\qquad
\begin{array}{r}
4\ \square\ \square \\
-\ 3\ 7\ 8 \\
\hline
5\ 4
\end{array}
$$

Workbook Exercise 24
Workbook Review 1

Unit 3 – Length

Objectives for the unit

- Recognize and use meters and centimeters as units of measurement.
- US: Recognize and use yards, feet, and inches as units of measurement.
- Estimate and measure length to the nearest given unit of measurement.
- Add and subtract lengths.
- Determine appropriate units of measurement for the length of an object.
- US: Compare a yard with a meter and an inch with a centimeter.
- Draw straight lines of a given length.

Suggested number of sessions: 6

	Objectives	Textbook	Workbook	Activities
Part 1 : Measuring Length in Meters				**2 sessions**
36	▪ Understand the meter as a unit of measurement. ▪ Estimate the length of an object as equal to, longer than, or shorter than 1 meter. ▪ Measure length to the nearest meter.	p. 52 p. 53, tasks 1-2	Ex. 25	3.1a
37	▪ Estimate lengths longer than a meter. ▪ Add or subtract lengths.	p. 54, tasks 3-5		3.1b
Part 2 : Measuring Length in Centimeters				**2 sessions**
38	▪ Understand the centimeter as a unit of measurement. ▪ Measure length to the nearest centimeter. ▪ Compare lengths in centimeters.	p. 55 p. 56, tasks 1-2	Ex. 26	3.2a
39	▪ Measure curved lengths. ▪ Use a measuring tape. ▪ Draw a straight line of a given length in centimeters.	pp. 57-58, tasks 3-7	Ex. 27 3dEx. 28	3.2b
US: Part 3 : Measuring Length in Yards and Feet				**1 session**
40	▪ Understand the yard and foot as units of measurement. ▪ Measure length to the nearest yard or foot. ▪ Compare a yard with a foot.	USpp. 59-60, tasks 1-4		3.3a
US: Part 4 : Measuring Length in Inches				**1 session**
41	▪ Understand the inch as a unit of measurement. ▪ Compare a foot with an inch. ▪ Measure length to the nearest inch. ▪ Compare a yard with a meter. ▪ Compare an inch with a centimeter.	USp. 61 USp. 61, task 1 USp. 62	USEx. 28	3.4a

Part 1: Measuring Length in Meters | **2 sessions**

Objectives

- Understand the meter as a unit of measurement.
- Estimate and measure to the nearest meter.
- Add and subtract lengths in meters.

Materials

- Items for non-standard measurement in two lengths, such as paper clips of two different lengths
- Meter stick
- String
- Word problems involving adding or subtracting length in meters
- Ribbon or string cut to lengths of 1 to 10 meters

Homework

- Workbook Exercise 25

Notes

In *Primary Mathematics 1*, students learned to measure and compare lengths using non-standard units such as paper clips or craft sticks. In this unit, standard lengths of measurements are introduced.

Students should be able to estimate the length of a unit of measurement. It is useful to have something familiar with which to compare the lengths. For example, a meter is about the length of a baseball bat, or about the width of a door. A centimeter is nearly the width (diameter) of a dime [10-cent coin], or the width of a finger. Make sure your students know that these references are only for approximations, not for actual measurements.

US:

Students may already be familiar with the U.S. standard units such as yards, feet, or inches. They will learn two systems of measurement, the metric system, and the U.S. customary system. Today, almost 95% of the world's population uses the metric system.

Students should understand that they are learning two systems of measurement, the metric system, which is used in most countries, and the system commonly used in the U.S. They need to be able to keep them separate. Lengths are measured in meters and centimeters, or in yards and feet and inches, but not in meters and inches at the same time. Emphasize which measurements are part of the metric system, and which are part of the U.S. customary system.

Activity 3.1a   Meters

1. Discuss the need for standard units of measurement.
   - Do some activities with your students to illustrate the importance of a standard unit of measurement. For example:
     o Give some students one size of paper clips and others a different size. Ask them to measure the length of their math books with paper clips. Compare the answers. Have students attempt to determine the reason for the differences in length.
     o Have some students remove their shoes and measure the length of something in "feet." Compare results and discuss reasons for different results.
   - Tell students that it is not possible to communicate exact measurements using body part sizes since their size depends on the measurer. Standard units of measurements were developed so that everyone would know and use the same unit of measurement.

2. Introduce the meter as a unit of measurement.
   - Show students a meter stick. Tell them that the meter is a standard unit of measurement in many countries.
   - Direct students' attention to the **textbook p. 52**. Have students compare their heights to a meter stick.
   - Provide some string and ask students to estimate a meter and cut a piece of string a meter long. Let them compare their cut string to a meter stick. Then have them each cut a length of string that is exactly 1 meter long (or provide them with string that is already cut to 1 meter).
   - Tell students that we can use **m** to stand for meters after a number, e.g., 1 m, 10 m.

3. Estimate and measure lengths as more than or less than one meter.
   - Point out lengths around the room and estimate whether they are longer or shorter or about the same as a meter, and then measure with the meter stick, or their string, as in the **tasks 2-3, textbook pp. 53-54**.
   - Do **Workbook Exercise 25 in the workbook** in class.

Activity 3.1b   Meters

1. Estimate and measure lengths longer than a meter to the nearest meter.
   - Have students estimate in meters a length that is longer than 1 meter, such as 10 meters.
     o You can put two objects 10 meters apart, ask students to tell you about how far apart they are in meters, and then have them measure the distance between them with a meter stick or string that has been cut to one meter.
     o They could estimate the length and width of the classroom and then measure to the nearest meter.

2. Estimate and measure lengths longer than a meter to the nearest meter.
   - Divide students into groups and give each group two ribbons cut to some multiple of 1 meter. They should measure and record the lengths of the ribbons, and then find how much longer or shorter one ribbon is than another, and the total length of both ribbons.
   - Discuss **tasks 3-5, textbook p. 54**. Point out, if necessary, that the lengths for meters in the text are not actual lengths, but have been scaled down, as with maps.
   - Provide some other word problems. Use some with 3-digit numbers. For example, "Janet ran 224 meters and then took a rest. She ran another 162 meters. If she has to run another 64 meters, how far does she run in all?"

| Part 2: Measuring Length in Centimeters | 2 sessions |

Objectives

- Understand the centimeter as a unit of measurement.
- Estimate and measure length to the nearest centimeter.
- Add and subtract lengths in centimeters.

Materials

- 20 cm strips of tag board or cardboard with centimeters marked
- Rulers (12 inch/30 cm) for each student
- Strips of paper, ribbon, or string cut to various lengths shorter than a meter
- Measuring tape, such as used in sewing, marked in centimeters
- Worksheet with curved lines
- Unmarked straight edge for each student
- Word problems involving addition or subtraction of lengths in centimeters

Homework

- Workbook Exercise 26
- Workbook Exercise 27

Notes

In this section, students will learn to measure lengths shorter than a meter in centimeters. They will be measuring to the nearest centimeter, since fractional lengths are not covered here. Students should use the words "about" or "almost" when measuring such lengths.

You may wish to tell students that a meter is 100 centimeters; however, at this level they will not be asked to convert between units of measurement.

Which is Longest?

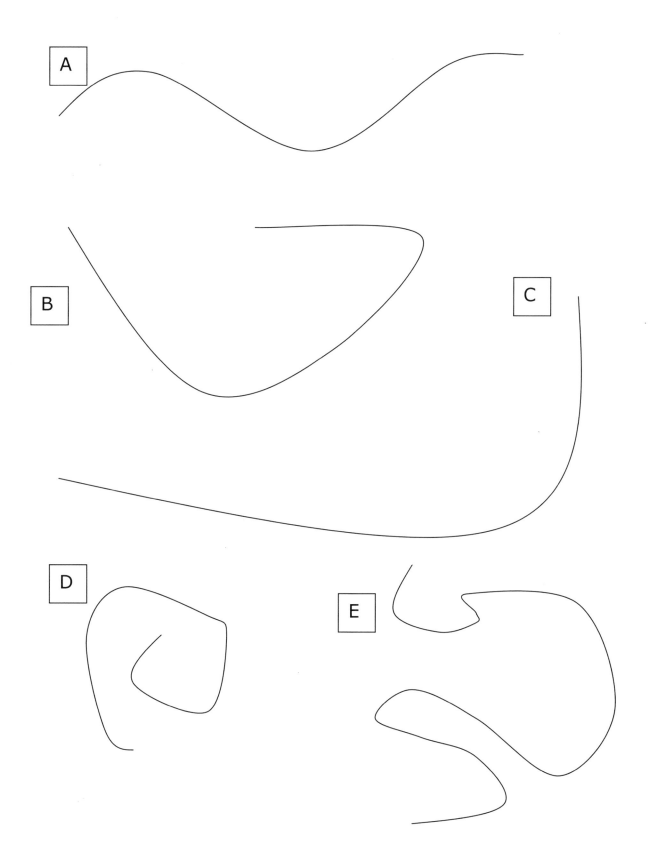

Activity 3.2a   **Centimeters**

1. Introduce the centimeter as a unit of measurement.
   - Tell students that we use another unit of measurement, the centimeter, to measure objects shorter than a meter. Provide students with strips marked in centimeters. Tell them each mark is a centimeter. Have them measure the width of their book or the length of their pencil to the nearest centimeter.
   - Provide each student with rulers.
     o Have students locate a centimeter on their rulers.
     o US: Point out that one side shows centimeters and the other inches, a different unit of measurement.
     o Have students line up the marks on their strips with the marks on the ruler. Point out that the longest mark on the centimeter side of the ruler is for centimeters. Also point out that some rulers do not start exactly at the beginning of the first centimeter. The 0 mark is sometimes a little ways in from the edge of the ruler.

2. Estimate and measure objects to the nearest centimeter.
   - Have the students look at the **textbook p. 55**.
     o Point out that we use **cm** to stand for centimeters.
     o Let them measure the length of the grasshopper and fish with their own rulers. They need to make sure they align the edge of the objects with the 0 mark on the ruler. Elicit answers to the rest of the page.
   - Have the students do **tasks 1-2, textbook p. 56** and **problem 1, Workbook Exercise 26**.
   - Do a length hunt. Call on students to find objects of a certain length, such as something that is about 8 cm long, somewhere in the classroom.

3. Add or subtract lengths in centimeters.
   - Give each group or pair of students two of the cut strips of paper, ribbon, or string and have them first estimate, and then measure each strip.
     o Ask them to find the difference in length.
     o Ask them to find the total length.
   - Discuss ways of measuring lengths in centimeters that are longer than the length of their rulers. Show them how they can measure up to 30 cm, or the maximum length on their rulers, make a mark or put their fingernail at the 30 cm length, and then move their rulers and continue measuring from the 0 mark, totaling the measurements. They may suggest using several rulers.
   - Show the centimeters on a meter stick. Have student measure other objects in the classroom that are longer than their rulers, but shorter than a meter.
   - Provide some word problems involving addition or subtraction of lengths in centimeters.

4. Choose an appropriate unit of measurement.
   - Point out certain objects, such as a tree or a book, and ask students if we would measure them in meters or centimeters.

Workbook Exercise 26

Activity 3.2b   **Centimeters**

1. Measure curved lengths.
   - Draw a curved line and ask students for suggestions on how to measure its length (the length it would be if it were stretched out into a straight line).
   - Have students do **tasks 3-5, textbook p. 57**. Point out that they can put the start of the string at the start of the line, then match up the string with the line by moving their fingers along the string. (The part of the string that has already been matched with the drawn curve can come off the line as they move their fingers along.) Then they mark the end on the string with a marker, or cut the string and measure its length.
   - You may want to give them more practice measuring curved lines. You can use the worksheet on p. 63 of this guide or one of your own, or have them measure some curved length in the classroom. For the worksheet, students can first order the lines from shortest to longest by estimation and then measure to see if their guess was correct.

2. Use a measuring tape.
   - Divide the students into groups and give each group a measuring tape.
   - Show students the centimeters on a measuring tape.
     - o Show them how to use the measuring tape to measure around something. Allow them to measure their own waists.
     - o They can record their results in **problem 1, Workbook Exercise 27**.
     - o Let them measure other parts of their bodies and record the measurements.

3. Draw lines of a given length.
   - Have students practice drawing some lines of given lengths in centimeters. They need to be careful to start at the 0 mark, and to not let the ruler slip as they draw the line.

   - Game:
     - o Divide the students into groups. Provide each student with an unmarked straight edge, such as a strip of cardboard.
     - o Students take turns calling out a length less than 30 centimeters. The rest of the students in the group draw a line that they think is that length using the unmarked straight edge. Each student then measures the length with a ruler. The player who comes closest to the desired length gets a point.

Workbook Exercise 26
3rd: Workbook Exercise 28

___

US: Part 3: Measuring Length in Yards and Feet	1 session

Objectives

- Understand the yard and the foot as units of measurement.
- Estimate and measure to the nearest yard or foot.
- Add and subtract lengths in yards or feet.
- Compare a meter to a yard.
- Compare a foot to a yard.

Materials

- Meter sticks
- Yard sticks
- Strips of thin cardboard exactly 1 foot long
- Rulers (1 foot)

Notes

In this section and the next, students will be using yards, feet, and inches as units of measurement. They should be able to estimate the lengths of these units. They can use references. For example, an inch is about the length of the last joint of a finger. Six inches may be about the length of their palm. A foot is about the length of a forearm.

Students will not be converting between different measurement systems in *Primary Mathematics*, but they should be able to understand the comparative sizes of the measurements. For example, a meter is a just a little longer than a yard. An inch is between two and three centimeters. A foot is about 30 centimeters long. A kilometer is a little more than half of a mile (kilometers and miles are taught *in Primary Mathematics 3B*, but they can be mentioned here if the subject comes up).

Conventions for abbreviations change over time. In these books, periods will not be used in the abbreviations (yd, ft, m, cm), except for the inch, which is still generally abbreviated with a period (in.).

Activity 3.3a   **Yards and Feet**

1. Introduce the yard and foot as a unit of measurement.

    *   Tell the students that in the U.S. we often measure lengths in yards and feet. Show them a yard stick. Compare its length to a meter stick to show that a yard is slightly shorter than a meter.

    *   Show them the 1-foot strip of cardboard. Tell them this is called a foot. Give each student or group of students one and have them measure it with their rulers. They should see that the 12 mark on the ruler on the side opposite the centimeters is one foot.

    *   Put two rulers next to each other to show two feet. Tell students that when we have more than one foot, we call them feet.

    *   Have students use their rulers or the strips to find the number of feet in a yard.

2. Estimate and measure length in yards or feet.

    *   Have students do the **tasks 1-4, textbook ᵁˢpp. 59-60**.

    *   Have students estimate and measure other objects in the room or outside, to the closest yard or foot, using string, yard sticks, and/or rulers.

    *   Challenge them to find an object of a certain number of feet.

    *   Provide some word problems involving addition or subtraction of lengths in yards or feet. For example: The length of a door is 9 feet and the width is 3 feet. How much longer is the length than the width?

| US: Part 4: Measuring Length in Inches | 1 session |

Objectives

- Understand the inch as a unit of measurement.
- Estimate and measure to the nearest inch.
- Add and subtract lengths in inches.
- Compare an inch to a centimeter.
- Compare an inch to a foot.

Materials

- Rulers (12 inches) for each student
- Ribbon or paper strips cut to different inches
- Word problems involving addition and subtraction of lengths in inches

Homework

- Workbook Exercise 28

Activity 3.4a   **Inches**

1. Introduce the inch as a unit of measurement.

   - Tell students that in the U.S. we often measure lengths shorter than a foot in inches. Show them an inch on the ruler. Tell them that there are 12 inches in a foot. Show them the inches on a yard stick and on a measuring tape.

2. Estimate and measure length in yards or feet.

   - Have students do the activities on **textbook ^{US}p. 61.**

   - Discuss the information on **textbook ^{US}p. 62.** Let the students use the ruler to tell you about how many centimeters are the same as a foot.

   - Have students estimate and measure other objects in the room to the closest inch. Provide them with yard sticks and measuring tapes to measure objects longer than 12 inches.

   - Challenge them to find an object of a certain length in inches.

   - Give students the strips of ribbon or paper and have them first estimate their lengths and then measure them.

   - Ask them to practice drawing lines of a certain number of inches.

   - Point out certain objects inside and outside the classroom and ask if they should be measured in yards, feet, or inches.

   - Provide students with string and have them measure some curved lines in inches.

   - Provide some word problems involving addition or subtraction of lengths in yards or feet.

Workbook Exercise 28

Review 2

Objectives

- Review previous topics

Suggested number of sessions: 1

	Objectives	Textbook	Workbook	Activities
42	▪ Review	US p. 63, Practice 3A ------------------------ 3d p. 59, Practice 3A	Review 2	R.2

Activity R.2   **Review**

1. Have students do **Practice 3A, textbook p. 63 [3ʳᵈ p. 59].**

2. Let students play some of the games from earlier units to review math facts.

Workbook Review 2

Unit 4 – Weight

Objectives for the unit

- Recognize and use kilograms and grams as units of measurement.
- US: Recognize and use pounds and ounces as units of measurement.
- Read scales.
- Estimate the weight of objects.
- Compare weights.
- Add and subtract weights.
- Compare a pound with a kilogram and an ounce with a gram.

Suggested number of sessions: 5

	Objectives	Textbook	Workbook	Activities
Part 1 : Measuring Weight in Kilograms				**2 sessions**
43	▪ Understand the kilogram as a unit of measurement. ▪ Weigh objects to the nearest kilogram.	US pp. 64 US p. 65, tasks 1-2(a) 3d p. 60 3d p. 61, tasks 1-2(a)		4.1a
44	▪ Read scales in kilograms. ▪ Compare weights. ▪ Add and subtract weights in kilograms.	US pp. 65-67, tasks 2(b)-7 3d pp. 61-63, tasks 2(b)-7	Ex. 29	4.1b
Part 2 : Measuring Weight in Grams				**1 session**
45	▪ Understand the gram as a unit of measurement. ▪ Read scales in grams. ▪ Weigh objects to the nearest 50 grams. ▪ Add and subtract weights in grams.	US pp. 68–69, tasks 1-3 3d pp. 64–65, tasks 1-3	Ex. 30	4.2a
US: Part 3 : Measuring Weight in Pounds				**1 session**
46	▪ Understand the pound as a unit of measurement. ▪ Read scales in pounds. ▪ Compare weights in pounds. ▪ Weigh objects to the nearest pound.	US p. 70 US pp. 70-71, tasks 1-4		4.3a
US: Part 4 : Measuring Weight in Ounces				**1 session**
47	▪ Understand the ounce as a unit of measurement. ▪ Read scales in ounces. ▪ Weigh objects to the nearest ounce. ▪ Compare pound with kilogram. ▪ Compare ounce with gram.	US p. 72 US pp. 72, tasks 1-2 US p. 73		4.4a

| **Part 1: Measuring Weight in Kilograms** | **2 sessions** |

Objectives

- Understand the kilogram as a unit of measurement.
- Estimate and weigh objects to the nearest kilogram.
- Add and subtract weights in kilograms.
- Read scales.

Materials

- Balance (one for each group)
- Kilogram weight (one for each group)
- Dried beans, sand, rice, paper clips, and other small objects
- Sealable bags (e.g. Ziploc bags)
- Various weighing scales
- Objects to weigh

Homework

- Workbook Exercise 29, #3-4

Notes

In *Primary Mathematics 1*, students learned to compare weights by feel or "heft" and to measure weight using nonstandard units such as marbles. This section introduces the kilogram as the standard unit of weight.

The kilogram and the gram (which is introduced in the next section) are actually units of measurement for mass, not weight. Mass is a measure of how much matter a body contains, that is, how much inertia it has. Weight, in contrast, is a measure of the gravitational pull between two objects. Mass is measured using a balance and comparing a known mass to an unknown mass. Weight is measured using a scale where the gravitational pull is calibrated. Some scales are calibrated for the equivalent mass on earth. The metric unit of weight is the Newton; on earth a mass of 1 kilogram weighs 9.8 Newtons.

US:

The pound and ounce, which will be introduced later, are measures of weight, not mass. Students do not need to distinguish between weight and mass here. Since they will be weighing objects, the term "weight" will be used for both the metric system and for the U.S. customary system.

Activity 4.1a   **Kilograms**

1. Introduce the kilogram as a unit of weight.
   - Discuss various ways in which weighing is used in everyday life. Ask students what types of things we weigh. Have them tell you why we weigh them.
   - Divide students into groups and give each group a balance. Ask them how they would weigh their math books and tell another group how much it weighs. Lead the discussion to a need for a standard unit of weights. Students might mention some standard units of weight they have already heard about.
   - Tell them a kilogram is the standard unit of weight in most countries. Have them handle a kilogram weight.
   - Tell them we write **kg** for kilogram.

2. Weigh objects to the nearest kilogram, using a balance.
   - Have students compare the weight of various objects to 1 kilogram. They should first "weigh" the object in their hands and guess whether it is heavier or lighter than a kilogram, and then compare it to a kilogram, as on the **textbook p. 64 [3rd p. 60]**.
   - You can have each student make weights of 1 kg, as **in task 1, textbook p. 65 [3rd p. 61]**. If possible, have different groups use different items to make their 1 kg bags (e.g. dried beans, dried peas, rice), and then compare the feel of 1 kg bags of different objects. They all weigh the same.
   - Ask students which weighs more, a kilogram of feathers or a kilogram of rocks?
   - Get students to use their balances and kilogram weights to find objects or a combination of objects that weigh about 1 kg.
   - Have students first estimate, and then measure, the weights of various objects to the nearest kg, as in **task 2(a), textbook p. 65 [3rd p. 61]**.
     - Have students record the weights of their objects in a table that you draw on the board. Keep the results for the next session.

Activity 4.1b   **Kilograms**

1. Read scales
   - Remind your student that in the previous activity they weighed objects against a known weight, using a balance.
   - Discuss other means of weighing, such as a bathroom scale or a produce scale.
     - Demonstrate how to read the scales with whatever scales that are available. Weigh the same object on different scales that use the same unit of weight. Show that the scales have been calibrated so that either the needle moves or the scale moves to the correct weight regardless of the scale used.
     - (US: If you are using scales calibrated in pounds, simply tell your students that a pound is another unit of weight that will be discussed later).

2. If you have enough scales, you can have students do **problem 1, Workbook Exercise 29**, in class.

3. Discuss **tasks 1-5, textbook pp. 65-66 [3rd pp. 61-62]**.
   - Draw students' attention to the scale on p. 65 [3rd p. 61]. Ask them how far around the needle needs to go to show a weight of 1 kg, 2 kg, 3 kg, or 4 kg. Point out that the needle will go all the way around for 4 kg. This scale cannot weigh objects that are more than 4 kg.
   - Have students supply the answers for tasks 2(b)-5.

4. Discuss **tasks 6-7, textbook p. 67 [3rd p. 63]**.
   - Draw students' attention to the two scales in task 6. Point out that the scales are different. You can draw some number lines with different scales and point out that the numbers are closer together on one line than on another.

   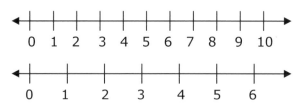

   - Ask students where the needle would point if the package with the blue ribbon were weighed on the second scale. Point out that would still point to the 4, but the needle would not have to go around as far.

5. Compare weights, add and subtract weights.
   - Use the results from the previous activity where students weighed objects to the nearest kilogram and recorded their results in a table on the board.
   - Ask students to order the objects from lightest to heaviest.
   - Ask students questions such as:
     o Which object weighed the least?
     o Which objects weighed the most?
     o How much more did the [book] weigh than the [sharpener]?
     o How much did they weigh altogether?
     o How much do [pick 3 objects] weigh altogether?
   - You can have students write appropriate equations.

   Workbook Exercise 29, problems 3-4

Part 1: Measuring Weight in Grams   1 session

Objectives

- Understand the gram as a unit of measurement.
- Estimate and measure objects in grams.
- Add and subtract weight in grams.

Materials

- Balance (one for each group)
- 20, 50 and 100 g weights, unit cubes from base-10 set (which weigh about 1 g)
- Pennies, beans, paper clips, Ziploc bags
- Electronic scale, if available
- Kitchen scales in grams, if available
- Food items such as tin cans or other items giving the weight in grams on the label
- Some objects weighed and labeled with their weight in grams

Homework

- Workbook Exercise 30, #2-3

Notes

In this section students will learn about the gram as a unit of measurement.

There are 1000 grams in a kilogram.

Students will not be converting between grams and kilograms at this level.

Activity 4.2a   **Grams**

1. Introduce the gram as a unit of weight.
   - Tell students that we use *grams* to weigh objects lighter than 1 kilogram. Show them a unit cube or two paper clips linked together and say that they weigh about 1 gram.
   - Discuss **textbook p. 68 [3rd p. 64]** (top of page). Have them feel the weight of various objects. (US: Two pennies are actually closer to 5 grams than 3 grams.)
   - If you have an electronic balance, let them weigh some small objects (marble, envelope, bean, etc.) to the nearest gram. (Balances or scales are not precise enough to weigh to the nearest gram
   - Have them handle and look at the weights of various foods or other objects where the weight is given in grams.

2. Read scales in grams.
   - Discuss **textbook p. 68 [3rd p. 64]** (bottom of page) and **tasks 1-2, textbook p. 69, [3rd p. 65]**.
     - Talk about the scale on each of the weighing scales.
     - Ask students how many subdivisions there are between each 100 grams and how many grams each subdivision stands for.
     - Ask them to locate 250 g on each of the scales on [US]p. 69, [3d]p.65.

3. Weigh objects to the nearest 50 grams.
   - Students can work in groups. If you have enough scales in grams, give each group a scale. Otherwise, give each group a balance and some weights (up to 50 g).
   - You can also give them some pennies or beans or other small objects, letting them make up additional weights of 50 grams by weighing some pennies or beans against the standard weights. About 20 pennies weigh 50 grams.
   - Have students do **task 3, textbook p. 69 [3rd p. 65]** and **problem 1, Workbook Exercise 30,** in class.
   - Have students first estimate and then weigh various objects which weigh less than 1 kg and record the weights. If using a bucket balance or scales other than an electronic balance, have them weigh the objects to the nearest 50 grams.
   - Tabulate some of their data. Ask questions involving finding the difference or the sum of the weights of two or three objects.

Workbook Exercise 30, #2-3

| **US: Part 3: Measuring Weight in Pounds** | **1 session** |

Objectives

- Understand the pound as a unit of measurement.
- Estimate and weigh objects to the nearest pound.
- Add and subtract weights in pounds.

Materials

- Balance (one for each group), or weighing scales in pounds
- Pound weight, kilogram weight (one for each group)
- Dried beans, rice, paper clips, and other small objects
- Sealable bags (e.g. Ziploc bags)

Notes

Students in the US are probably more familiar with pounds than kilograms. Since students will be seeing problems later involving the weight of people, you may want to point out that 2 pounds are about the same as 1 kilogram. (1 kg = 2.205 pounds) A person weighing 30 kilograms weighs about 60 pounds. So if they see the weight of a person in kilograms, they can double it to get the approximate weight in pounds. So if they know their weight in pounds, and get a problem where a child weighs about half that much in kilograms, the child is actually about their size.

Activity 4.3a   **Pounds**

1. Introduce the pound as a unit of weight.

   - Tell students that the pound is the unit of weight commonly used in the United States. Discuss instances when they may have heard about things being weighed in pounds. Most students will know about how much they weigh in pounds.

2. Estimate and measure objects to the nearest pound.

   - Divide students into groups. Provide each group with a balance and a pound weight.

   - Students can weigh different objects to see if they are more or less than a pound.

   - To get additional pound weights, you can have them make up pound weights with a bag and small objects such as beans, as on **textbook p. 70**.

   - Have students weigh various objects to the nearest pound.

   - Tabulate some of the data and lead students to find the differences or the sum of some of the weights.

   - You may also give each group a kilogram weight or have them use some of the kilogram weights they made previously. Let them compare a pound to a kilogram and see which is heavier.

3. Have students do **tasks 2-3, textbook p. 71**.

US: Part 4: Measuring Weight in Ounces	1 session

Objectives

- Understand the ounce as a unit of measurement.
- Estimate and weigh to the nearest ounce.
- Add and subtract weights in ounces.

Material

- Balance (one for each group), or weighing scales in ounces
- Ounce weight, pound weight (one for each group)
- Pennies, paper clips, other small objects, tape
- Food items such as tin cans or other items giving the weight in ounces on the label

Notes

In this section, students will become familiar with the ounce as a unit of measurement. Students can compare an ounce to a pound (and to a gram) but they will not be converting between ounces and pounds and do not need to know exact conversion units. An ounce is about 28 grams (1 oz = 28.35 grams) and so is quite a bit heavier than a gram.

Activity 4.4a   **Ounces**

1. Introduce the ounce as a unit of weight.
   - Tell your student that the ounce is the unit of weight commonly used in the United States for weighing objects less than a pound. Have them look at the labels on various food items where the weight is given in ounces. They can compare the ounce weight to the gram weight given on the can.

2. Have students read the scales in **task 1, textbook p. 72**.

3. Weigh objects to the nearest ounce.
   - Divide students into groups. Provide each group with an ounce scale, or a balance and an ounce weight.
   - Have students make one ounce weights from pennies, connect-a-cubes or other objects. About 11 pennies make up an ounce. They can tape the pennies together in a stack to get ounce weights.
   - Students estimate and weigh various objects less than a pound and record their weights. Bucket balances may not be precise enough to get accurate weights to the nearest ounce. You may want to discuss why different groups may be getting different weights.

4. Discuss **textbook p. 73**.
   - A pound is lighter than a kilogram. (It is about half a kilogram). A gram is quite a bit lighter than an ounce.
   - You can have students use weights and balances to compare pounds with kilograms and grams with ounces. They can see about how many grams weight the same as an ounce.

5. Review the units of measurement studied so far.
   - Remind students that meters and centimeters are used for measuring length in the metric system. Yards, feet, and inches are used for measuring length in the U.S. standard system.
   - Ask students to point out some objects that have lengths of approximately one meter, one centimeter, one yard, one foot, or one inch.
   - Remind students that kilograms and grams are used for measuring weight in the metric system. Pounds and ounces are used for measuring weight in the standard U.S. system.
   - Ask students to name some objects that weigh close to one kilogram, one gram, one pound, or one ounce.

Review 3

Objectives

- Review previous topics.

Suggested number of sessions: 3

	Objectives	Textbook	Workbook	Activities
48 49 50	▪ Review	US p. 74, Practice 4A US p. 75, Review A 3d p. 66, Practice 4A 3d p. 67, Review A	Review 3 Review 4	R.3

Activity R.3   **Review**

1. Have students do **Practice 4A, textbook p. 74 [3ʳᵈ p. 68]** and **Review A, textbook p. 75 [3ʳᵈ p. 67]** and share their solutions.

2. Play games or do fact practice from previous units.

Workbook Review 3
Workbook Review 4

Unit 5 – Multiplication and Division

Objectives for the unit

- Review the concept of multiplication as repeated addition.
- Use rectangular arrays to illustrate multiplication.
- Review the concept of division as sharing or grouping.
- Write equations for multiplication and division.
- Use pictures to solve word problems which involve multiplication and division.

Suggested number of sessions: 7

	Objectives	Textbook	Workbook	Activities
Part 1 : Multiplication				**3 sessions**
51	▪ Understand the meaning of multiplication. ▪ Write equations for multiplication.	^US^p. 76 ^US^pp. 77-78, tasks 1-3 ^3d^p. 68 ^3d^pp. 69-70, tasks 1-3	Ex. 31, 32	5.1a
52	▪ Use rectangular arrays to illustrate multiplication. ▪ Write two related equations for a multiplication situation.	^US^p. 78, task 4 ^3d^p. 70, task 4	Ex. 33, 34	5.1b
53	▪ Solve word problems on multiplication using pictures. ▪ Work out multiplication facts by repeated addition.	^US^p. 79, Practice 5A ^3d^p. 71, Practice 5A		5.1c
Part 2 : Division				**4 sessions**
54	▪ Understand division as sharing equally into a given number of groups and finding the number in each group. ▪ Write equations for division by sharing.	^US^pp. 81-82, tasks 1-3 ^3d^pp. 73-74, tasks 1-3	Ex. 35, 36	5.2a
55	▪ Understand division as dividing a set of objects into groups of equal size and finding the number of groups. ▪ Write equations for division by grouping.	^US^p. 80 ^US^pp. 83-84, tasks 4-6 ^3d^p. 72 ^3d^pp. 75-76, tasks 4-6	Ex. 37, 38	5.2b
56	▪ Form a family of two multiplication equations and two division equations.	^US^p. 85, tasks 7-8 ^3d^p. 77, tasks 7-8	Ex. 39	5.2c
57	▪ Review.	^US^p. 86, Practice 5B ^US^p. 87, Practice 5C ^3d^p. 78, Practice 5B ^3d^p. 79, Practice 5C	Review 5	5.2d

| Part 1: Multiplication | 3 sessions |

Objectives

- Understand the meaning of multiplication.
- Write equations for multiplication.
- Work out multiplication facts by repeated addition.
- Solve word problems involving multiplication using pictures.
- Write two related equations for a multiplication situation.

Materials

- Counters or other objects that can be displayed
- Counters for students
- Connect-a-cubes for students
- One number cube labeled with 1-6 and one with 4-9, for each group
- Number cards 1-9, four sets for each group
- Centimeter graph paper, other grid paper, or the backs of laminated hundreds boards and dry-erase markers for each student
- Sheets of stickers

Homework

- Workbook Exercise 31
- Workbook Exercise 32
- Workbook Exercise 33
- Workbook Exercise 34

Notes

Students were introduced to the concept of multiplication as repeated addition in *Primary Mathematics 1*. This is reviewed in this section. The emphasis in this section is on understanding multiplication, not on memorizing the multiplication facts. Allow students to use manipulatives and repeated addition to solve the multiplication problems in this section.

Multiplication is associated with the part-whole concept. Given the number of equal parts and the number in each part, we can multiply to find the whole (the total).

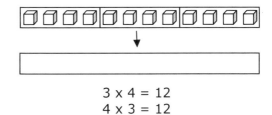

3 x 4 = 12
4 x 3 = 12

"3 groups of 4" can be written as 3 x 4 or 4 x 3. Do not teach students that the first number has to be the number of groups. Students have learned in *Primary Mathematics 1* that 3 groups of 4 and 4 groups of 3 give the same answer, and that the order of the factors is not important. 4 x 3 could just as well be read as "4 each in 3 groups". By the time students learn algebra, there will be no arbitrarily imposed order to the factors determined by which one is the number of parts and which one is the number in each parts.

Activity 5.1a   **Multiplication as repeated addition**

1. Review the concept of multiplication.
   - Display objects, such as counters, in groups, e.g., 3 groups of 5.
   - Ask questions such as:
     - How many groups are there?
     - How many counters are there in each group?
     - How can we find how many counters there are altogether?
   - Lead students to see that rather than simply counting from 1 to 15, we can add 5 three times (starting from 0: 0 + 5 + 5 + 5)
   - Ask students if they remember what symbol we use to show that we are adding 5 three times. Write the multiplication equation 5 x 3 = 15. Discuss different ways to express 5 x 3:
     - 5 in 3 groups
     - 5 times 3
     - 5 multiplied by 3
     - multiply 5 by 3
   - Remind them that we can also write this as 3 x 5 = 15 and think of it as 3 groups of 5.
   - Be sure the students see the difference between the two symbols "+" and "x".
     - 5 + 3 means that there are two parts, one a 5 and one a 3, and we add each part together to get the whole.
     - 5 x 3 means there are 3 parts of 5 each.
   - Do some other examples.

$$5 + 5 + 5 = 15$$

$$5 \times 3 = 15$$

$$3 \times 5 = 15$$

2. Discuss **textbook p. 76 [3rd p. 68]** and **tasks 1-3, textbook pp. 77-78 [3rd pp. 69-70]**.

3. Write multiplication equations.
   - Pass out pages of stickers for students to share. Have them arrange like stickers on a page in groups and then write a multiplication equation for their pictures. They can illustrate their pictures. For example, group stickers of flowers into vases or stickers of cars in different lanes.

Workbook Exercises 31-32

Activity 5.1b   **Rectangular arrays**

1. Use rectangular arrays to illustrate multiplication.
   - Display objects, such as the units from base-10 blocks, in two equivalent rectangular arrays, or draw them on the board.
     - Draw lines to group the objects in one array into rows, and those in the other array into columns.
     - Using the first group, where the array is in rows, ask questions such as:
       - How many rows are there? (3)
       - How many objects are in each row? (4)
       - How many objects are there altogether? (12)
     - Write the addition equation on the board under this first group.

$$4 + 4 + 4 = 12$$

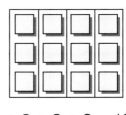

- o Using the second group, where the array is in columns, ask questions such as:
    - ➢ How many columns are there? (4)
    - ➢ How objects are there in each column? (3)
    - ➢ How many objects are there altogether? (12)
- o Write the addition equation on the board under the second group.
- o Ask student what two multiplication equations we can write to show the total number.

$$3 + 3 + 3 + 3 = 12$$

$$4 \times 3 = 12$$
$$3 \times 4 = 12$$

- • Lead students to see that to solve a multiplication equation such as 4 x 3 they can either add 4 three times (4 + 4 + 4) or add 3 four times (3 + 3 + 3 + 3).
- • Give them a multiplication situation, such as 8 x 2. Illustrate it with an array. Ask them whether it is easier to find the answer using 2 + 2 + 2 + 2 + 2 + 2 + 2 + 2 or 8 + 8.

2. Discuss task **4, textbook p. 78, [3ʳᵈ p. 70]**.

3. Game
- • Divide students into groups. Provide each group with two number cubes, one labeled with 1-6 and the other with 4-9, or four sets of number cards 1-9. Give each group connect-a-cubes or hundreds boards (they use the reverse side) and dry erase markers, or centimeter graph paper.
- • Each player throws both number cubes, or, from the number cards, draws 2 cards. They form an array using the two numbers. They write 2 equations for the array and determine the answer.

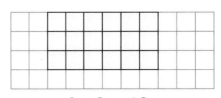

$$6 \times 3 = 18$$
$$3 \times 6 = 18$$

Workbook Exercises 33-34

Activity 5.1c   **Practice**

1. Use pictures or manipulatives to solve multiplication problems.
- • Provide each student with counters, connect-a-cubes, or other manipulatives. They could also simply draw simple pictures (see the game in item 3 on the next page). Write multiplication facts on the board and have the students work out the answer, using manipulatives. They should find the answer by forming groups and using repeated addition, rather than simply counting on. Call on students to explain how they arrived at their answer.
- • Tell the class multiplication stories. Students may work out their answers using manipulatives. For example:
    - o How many legs are there on 4 chairs?
    - o There are 4 boxes. Each has 5 cookies. How many cookies are there altogether?
    - o How many legs do three spiders have?
    - o How many legs do six mice have?
    - o I went for a walk and saw 9 people. They all had gotten so hot that they took off their shoes to dangle their feet in a fountain. A dog hid all their shoes. How many shoes did he hide?
- ▪ Call on students to make up multiplication stories for the other students to solve.

2. Have students do the problems in **Practice 5A, textbook p. 79 [3rd p. 71]**.

3. Game
    *   Divide students into groups. Give each group a
        number cube (labeled with 1 to 6).
    *   Each player throws the number cube once. They
        then draw the corresponding number of circles.
    *   Each player throws the number cube again. They
        draw the corresponding number of X's in each circle.
    *   Players then write a multiplication equation and find
        the total number of X's using repeated addition.
    *   For example, on the first throw a player gets a 4 and
        draws 4 circles. On the next throw, the player gets a
        3 and draws 3 X's in each circle. They write 4 x 3
        and find the answer using repeated addition.

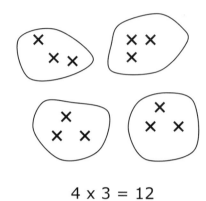

$$4 \times 3 = 12$$

Part 2: Division	**4 sessions**

Objectives

- Understand division as sharing equally into a given number of groups.
- Understand division as dividing a set of objects into groups of equal size.
- Write division equations.
- Solve world problems involving division, using pictures.
- Write two division and two multiplication equations for a given situation.
- Review.

Materials

- Counters or other objects that can be displayed
- Counters for students
- Connect-a-cubes for students
- Small paper plates or loops of yarn
- One number cube labeled with 1-6 and one with 4-9, for each group
- Number cards 1-9, four sets for each group
- Centimeter graph paper or other grid paper, or the backs of laminated hundreds boards and dry-erase markers for each student
- Straws, toothpicks, counting sticks, or craft sticks
- Rulers
- String or ribbon

Homework

- Workbook Exercise 35
- Workbook Exercise 36
- Workbook Exercise 37
- Workbook Exercise 38
- Workbook Exercise 39
- Review 5

Notes

Students were introduced to the concept of division in Primary Mathematics 1. This section is a review. The emphasis is on understanding the meaning of division rather than on memorization of division facts or on finding division facts from multiplication facts. Allow students to use pictures or manipulatives to solve all problems in this section.

The division symbol ($\div$) is introduced in this section.

Page 80 in the text illustrates two kinds of division situations:

> Sharing:
> Start with a set of objects (12 balloons).
> Make a given number of equal groups (3 groups).
> Find the number of objects in each group (4 balloons).

> Grouping:
> Start with a set of objects (12 balloons).
> Make equal groups of a given size (4 balloons in each group).
> Find the number of groups made (3 groups).

Previously, students learned that addition and subtraction are associated with the part-whole concept. If we are given two parts, we can add to find the whole. If we are given the whole and a part, we can subtract to find the other part.

Multiplication and division are also associated with the part-whole concept. Instead of two different parts making a whole, a specified number of equal parts make the whole.

Given the number of equal parts and the number in each part, we can multiply to find the whole (total).

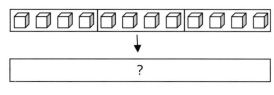

$$3 \times 4 = 12$$

Given the whole and the number of parts, we can divide to find the number in each part (sharing).

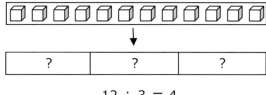

$$12 \div 3 = 4$$

Given the whole and the number in each part, we can divide to find the number of parts (grouping).

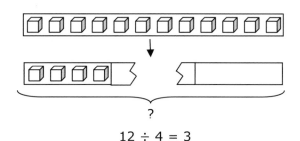

$$12 \div 4 = 3$$

In *Primary Mathematics 3*, students will be introduced to the term "unit" for the equal parts. At this level, they should understand that both multiplication and division are associated with equal parts.

Activity 5.2a   **Division by sharing**

1. Illustrate division by sharing.
   - Provide students with objects such as connect-a-cubes or counters, and small paper plates or loops of yarn.
   - Tell students to count out 12 objects and set out 3 paper plates or loops of yarn. Ask them to put an equal number of objects in each loop. Tell them they are sharing, or dividing, the objects equally into three groups. Ask how many are in each group.

   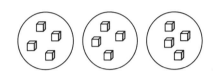

   $12 \div 3 = 4$

   - Tell students that the symbol we use to show that we are dividing is "÷". Write the division equation.
   - Tell them we can write the equation $12 \div 3 = 4$ to show what we did. Here the equation means 12 divided into 3 equal groups is 4 in each group.

   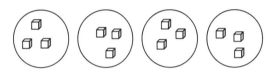

   $12 \div 4 = 3$

   - Ask students to now divide the 12 objects into 4 equal groups. How many are in each group? Have them write the corresponding equation. In this equation, 12 is the total number of objects. 4 is the number of equal groups we are dividing them into. 3, the answer, is the number that goes into each group.
   - Do some additional examples.

2. Discuss **task 1, textbook p. 81 [3rd p. 73]**
   - Have students do **tasks 2-3, textbook p. 82 [3rd p. 74]**.

3. Write equations for division by sharing.
   - Give students other division situations where a total is divided into a given number of groups. Have them work out the situation with objects. Direct them in writing the division equation. For example:
     ➢ You have 15 cookies and want to divide them up among yourself and two friends. How many would each of you get?
     ➢ There are 20 children in a class. They need to form 5 groups. How many children would be in each group?
   - Make sure your students understand the meaning of the different operation symbols. Write the following equations and have them illustrate them with their objects or with drawings:
     ○ 8 + 2
     ○ 8 − 2
     ○ 8 x 2
     ○ 8 ÷ 2

Workbook Exercises 35-36

Activity 5.2b   **Division by grouping**

1. Illustrate division grouping.
   - Provide each students with small objects such as connect-a-cubes or counters.
   - Ask 8 students to come to the front of the room. Tell them to make groups of 2 children each. Ask other students how many groups there are.
   - Illustrate the same situation with objects. We want to form equal groups with 2 in each group. How many groups do we have?
   - Write the division equation $8 \div 2 = 4$. Tell students that we also use division when we have a total and know how many go into each group. The answer is the number of groups we need. $8 \div 2 = 4$ can mean divide 8 into groups of 2 make 4 groups.
   - Have them find $8 \div 2$ by sharing; that is, making two groups. The answer is the same. So we use the division sign for both.
   - Ask students to each count out 15 objects and divide them into groups of 5. How many groups are there? Tell them they are grouping by 5. Write the equation on the board: $15 \div 5 = 3$.
   - Now ask students to divide the 15 objects into groups of 3. How many groups are there? Now they are grouping by 3. Write the equation on the board: $15 \div 3 = 5$.
   - Do some additional examples.

2. Discuss **task 4, textbook p. 83 [3rd p. 75]**
   - Have students do **tasks 5-6, textbook p. 84 [3rd p. 76]**.
   - Discuss **textbook p.80 [3rd p. 72]**. Note that the boy is sharing 12 balloons into 3 equal groups. Ask how many are in each group? (4) The girl is grouping the balloons by 4. How many groups does she have? (3)

3. Write equations for division by grouping.
   - Give students division situations where the number in each group must be found. Emphasize that they are finding equal groups. Students work out the problems with their objects and write the corresponding division equations. For example:
     ➢ You have 16 cookies. You want to put 4 cookies on each plate. How many plates do you need?
     ➢ There are 30 students in a class. You need to make teams of 6 children each. How many teams are there?
     ➢ You see 12 feet under a curtain. How many people are hiding behind the curtain?
     ➢ You have 27 wheels. How many tricycles can you make?

Workbook Exercises 37-38

Activity 5.2c   **Multiplication and division**

1. Write two multiplication and two division equations for a given situation.

    *   Provide students with connect-a-cubes or other cubes.

    *   Display 12 objects, such as the units from base-10 blocks, in an array. Ask questions such as:

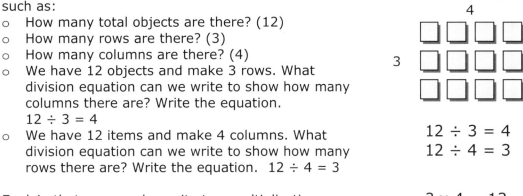

        o How many total objects are there? (12)
        o How many rows are there? (3)
        o How many columns are there? (4)
        o We have 12 objects and make 3 rows. What division equation can we write to show how many columns there are? Write the equation. $12 \div 3 = 4$
        o We have 12 items and make 4 columns. What division equation can we write to show how many rows there are? Write the equation. $12 \div 4 = 3$

    $$12 \div 3 = 4$$
    $$12 \div 4 = 3$$

    *   Explain that we can also write two multiplication equations for this arrangement. Ask students for the equations.

    $$3 \times 4 = 12$$
    $$4 \times 3 = 12$$

    *   Tell students to count out 20 items and arrange them into 4 rows. Ask them to write two division equations and two multiplication equations for the situation shown.

    *   Discuss **tasks 7-8, textbook p. 85 [3rd p. 77]**.

    *   Write a multiplication or division problem on the board, e.g. 3×9 or $24 \div 6$. Have students work out the answer with their objects by arranging the objects in a rectangular array and write the other three related equations. Illustrate the first one, if necessary, and give additional problems as necessary.

Workbook Exercise 39

___

Activity 5.2d   **Review**

1. Have students do **Practice 5B, textbook p. 86 [3rd p. 78]** and **Practice 5C, textbook p. 87 [3rd p. 79]** and discuss their solutions.

2. Optional: Investigations.
   - Divide students into groups or have them work individually. Provide each group (or student) with connect-a-cubes or counters. Tell them to start with 48 cubes. They must see how many rectangular arrays they can form. They should write two division equations and two multiplication equations for each array. They will see that some arrays are duplications (same number of rows and columns) so that they end up with 5 different sets of four equations.
   - Provide each group, or student, with straws (or toothpicks or counting sticks or craft sticks). Tell them to start by counting out 36 straws (by making 3 groups of 10 and 6 more). Ask them to find out how many separate squares they can make (each square is formed from four straws).
     o   Then find out how many separate triangles they can make from the 36 straws.
     o   What other shapes can they make using the same number of straws for each shape?
     o   Have them write the corresponding division equations.
     o   Let them try with other total amounts, making equal shapes. They may note that some total amounts won't divide into equal groups (e.g., prime numbers).
   - Review the different units of measurement learned so far. Ask for answers to problems involving lengths or weights. Include some division or multiplication problems, but only ask problems they can act out, and provide students with material to do so. For example:
     o   A string 12 inches long is cut into equal parts, each 2 inches long. How many equal parts are there?
     o   A string 10 inches long is cut into two equal parts. How long is each part?

Unit 6 – Multiplication Tables of 2 and 3

Objectives for the unit

- Count by twos and threes.
- Build multiplication tables for 2 and 3.
- Memorize multiplication facts for 2 and 3.
- Solve word problems involving multiplication by 2 or 3.
- Relate division by 2 or 3 to multiplication by 2 or 3.
- Memorize division facts for 2 and 3.
- Solve word problems involving division by 2 or 3.

Suggested number of lessons: 19

	Objectives	Textbook	Workbook	Activities
Part 1 : Multiplication Table of 2				**5 sessions**
58	▪ Count by twos. ▪ Relate counting by 2's to multiplication by 2.	pp. 88-89 p. 90, task 1 pp. 80-81 p. 82, task 1	Ex. 40-41	6.1a
59	▪ Build multiplication table of 2.	pp. 90-91, tasks 2-4 pp. 82-83, tasks 2-4	Ex. 42-43	6.1b
60	▪ Relate multiplication by 2 to doubling in addition. ▪ Write two multiplication equations for each fact.	pp. 91-92, tasks 5-8 pp. 83-84, tasks 5-8	Ex. 44	6.1c
61	▪ Practice multiplication facts for 2.	p. 93, Practice 6A, #1-5 p. 85, Practice 6A, #1-5	Ex. 45	6.1d
62	▪ Solve word problems which involve multiplication by 2.	p. 92, task 9 p. 93, Practice 6A, #6-10 p. 84, task 9 p. 85, Practice 6A, #6-10	Ex. 46	6.e
Part 2 : Multiplication Table of 3				**6 sessions**
63	▪ Count by threes.	pp. 94-95, task 1 pp. 86-87, task 1	Ex. 47-48	6.2a
64	▪ Write two multiplication equations for each fact.	p. 96, tasks 2-3 p.88, tasks 2-3	Ex. 49	6.2b
65	▪ Build multiplication table of 3. ▪ Relate facts for 3 more and 3 less.	p. 96, tasks 4-6 p. 99, tasks 4-6	Ex. 51-52	6.2c
66	▪ Memorize multiplication facts for 3.	p. 98, Practice 6B, #1-5 p. 90, Practice 6B, #1-5	Ex. 50, 53	6.2d
67	▪ Solve word problems which involve multiplication by 3.	p. 97, task 7 p. 98, Practice 6B, #6-10 p. 89, task 7 p. 90, Practice 6B, #6-10	Ex. 54	6.2e
68	▪ Review multiplication facts for 2 and 3.	p. 99, Practice 6C p. 91, Practice 6C	Ex. 55	6.2f

	Objectives	Textbook	Workbook	Activities
Part 3 : Dividing by 2				**3 sessions**
69	▪ Relate division facts to multiplication facts for 2.	pp. 100-101, tasks 1-2	Ex. 56, #1	6.3a
70	▪ Memorize division facts for 2.	p. 104, Practice 6D, #1-5	Ex. 56, #2	6.3b
71	▪ Solve word problems which involve division by 2.	pp. 102-103, tasks 3-6 p. 104, Practice 6D, #6-10	Ex. 57	6.3c
Part 4 : Dividing by 3				**5 sessions**
72	▪ Relate division facts to multiplication facts for 3.	p. 105, task 1	Ex. 58, #1	6.4a
73	▪ Memorize division facts for 3.	p. 107, Practice 6E, #1-5	Ex. 58, #2	6.4b
74	▪ Solve word problems which involve division by 3.	p. 106, tasks 2-3 p. 107, Practice 6E, #6-10	Ex. 59	6.4c
75 76	▪ Practice.	p. 108, Practice 6F	Ex. 60-62	6.4d

Mental Math 9

1.   1 x 2 = _____

2.   2 x 3 = _____

3.   3 x 2 = _____

4.   7 x 2 = _____

5.   9 x 2 = _____

6.   2 x 4 = _____

7.   2 x 8 = _____

8.   5 x 2 = _____

9.   2 x 6 = _____

10.   1 x 3 = _____

11.   2 x 9 = _____

12.   6 x 2 = _____

13.   8 x 1 = _____

14.   1 x 6 = _____

15.   10 x 2 = _____

16.   2 x 5 = _____

17.   1 x 7 = _____

18.   2 x 10 = _____

19.   8 x 2 = _____

20.   2 x 9 = _____

21.   2 x 7 = _____

22.   4 x 2 = _____

23.   4 x 1 = _____

24.   2 x 8 = _____

25.   7 x 2 = _____

26.   9 x 2 = _____

27.   5 x 1 = _____

28.   10 x 2 = _____

29.   20 x 2 = _____

30.   30 x 2 = _____

Mental Math 10

X	1	2	3	4	5	6	7	8	9	10
1										
2										
3										
4										
5										
6										
7										
8										
9										
10										

Mental Math 11

1. $1 \times 3 =$ _____
2. $4 \times 3 =$ _____
3. $3 \times 4 =$ _____
4. $3 \times 6 =$ _____
5. $2 \times 3 =$ _____
6. $7 \times 3 =$ _____
7. $3 \times 5 =$ _____
8. $3 \times 8 =$ _____
9. $3 \times 10 =$ _____
10. $9 \times 3 =$ _____
11. $2 \times 9 =$ _____
12. $3 \times 3 =$ _____
13. $7 \times 2 =$ _____
14. $2 \times 5 =$ _____
15. $7 \times 3 =$ _____

16. $6 \times 2 =$ _____
17. $8 \times 2 =$ _____
18. $3 \times 1 =$ _____
19. $3 \times 7 =$ _____
20. $3 \times 8 =$ _____
21. $5 \times 3 =$ _____
22. $6 \times 3 =$ _____
23. $3 \times 9 =$ _____
24. $3 \times 5 =$ _____
25. $3 \times 2 =$ _____
26. $8 \times 3 =$ _____
27. $3 \times 3 =$ _____
28. $10 \times 3 =$ _____
29. $20 \times 3 =$ _____
30. $30 \times 3 =$ _____

Multiplication by 2 or 3 Game Board

21	16	9	4	12	18
24	2	14	27	30	15
20	16	18	3	6	2
4	8	6	12	12	24
10	18	21	18	10	6
12	9	27	20	15	30
6	3	8	27	14	2

Part 1: Multiplication Table of 2	**5 sessions**

Objectives

- Count by twos.
- Build multiplication table of 2.
- Memorize multiplication facts for 2.
- Relate multiplication by 2 to doubling in addition.
- Write two multiplication equations for a rectangular array.
- Practice multiplication facts for 2.
- Solve word problems involving multiplication by 2.

Materials

- Counters or other objects that can be displayed
- Dot stickers
- Hundreds boards for students
- Counters for students
- Hundreds board that can be displayed
- Number cards 1-10, 4 sets for each group
- Fact cards

Homework

- Workbook Exercise 40
- Workbook Exercise 41
- Workbook Exercise 42
- Workbook Exercise 43
- Workbook Exercise 44
- Workbook Exercise 45
- Workbook Exercise 46

Notes

In this section, students will begin to study and commit multiplication facts to memory. Here they will learn to count by twos, relate counting by twos to multiplication by two, and memorize the multiplication facts for 2 through 2 x 10.

US:
You may also wish to include 2 x 11 and 2 x 12, since students in the U.S. will encounter twelves frequently (e.g., there are 12 inches in a foot; food items such as eggs are packed in twelves). However, multiplication of a 2-digit number by a 1-digit number (e.g., 12 x 2) will be covered in *Primary Mathematics 3*.

Activity 6.1a   **Count by 2's**

1. Practice counting by twos.
   - Display ten sets of two using counters or draw objects on the board in pairs. Ask students how many objects there are. Tell them we can count the number of objects by adding 2 to each number above it. Write the results for counting by 2 next to the objects. Have students practice counting their twos.
   - Provide students with dot stickers and an index card. Have them put their stickers on paper in two columns and then write the total amount, moving down the column, next to each pair.
   - Then have them cover up all except the top line (dot stickers and number) with an index card. Illustrate the process. They can move the card down one row at the time, and give the total number of stickers each time, by counting by twos. Have them try to say the next number under the card before uncovering it.
   - Provide students with a hundreds board and opaque counters. Have the students cover up the 1, 3, 5, etc. (odd numbers). Illustrate with an overhead hundreds board. Discuss any patterns they may see. For example, each uncovered number in the second row is ten more than the number in the first row.
   - Have students practice counting by 2's up to 20 both forwards and backwards.
   - Then have them remove the counters and cover up the 2's (even numbers), and again practice counting by 2's by saying the numbers that are covered up.
   - Have them practice without looking at the hundreds board.
   - Students should recognize whether a number is in the 2's sequence or not. Give them some numbers and ask them if the number is in the 2's sequence. For example, 8 is in the sequence, but 13 is not.
   - Continue to practice counting by twos now and again until students can do it easily forwards and backwards between 0 and 20.
   - Discuss **textbook p. 88 [3rd p. 80]**. Ask questions such as:
     o How many children are in each spaceship?
     o How many children are there in 2 spaceships?
     o How many children are there in 6 spaceships?

2. Write multiplication equations for situations involving counting by 2.
   - Display 4 sets of two. Ask how many there are. Point out that by counting by twos, we are adding two each time. Ask them for a multiplication sentence showing that we have 2 four times.
   - Discuss **textbook p. 89 [3rd p. 81]** and **task 1, textbook p. 90 [3rd p. 82]**. Students supply the answers.

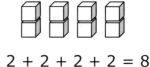

$$2 + 2 + 2 + 2 = 8$$
$$2 \times 4 = 8$$

Workbook Exercises 40-41

Column of pairs with counts:
⚪⚪ 2
⚪⚪ 4
⚪⚪ 6
⚪⚪ 8
⚪⚪ 10
⚪⚪ 12
⚪⚪ 14
⚪⚪ 16
⚪⚪ 18
⚪⚪ 20

Activity 6.1b   **Multiplication table for 2**

1. Build the multiplication table for 2.
   - Display two objects. Write a multiplication equation next to them.
     - o Add two more objects underneath the first two and ask students for the multiplication equation that will give the total number of objects. Stress the idea that the answer to the next equation is 2 more than the previous one.
     - o Continue adding objects in twos and writing the equations.
   - Have students also write the equations in a list, as in **task 4, textbook p. 91 [3ʳᵈ p. 83]**.
   - Now take away two at a time and show how each equation is two less than the one after it.
   - Tell students that they will be memorizing the "math facts" for multiplication, as they did for addition and subtraction, so that they can give the answer to a problem such as 2 x 8 without having to count by twos. Call out some math facts for multiplication by two so students can see that they may have already memorized some of them.

   2 x 1 = 2 $\Big)$ +2 $\Big)$ -2
   2 x 2 = 4 $\Big)$ +2 $\Big)$ -2
   2 x 3 = 6 $\Big)$ +2 $\Big)$ -2
   2 x 4 = 8 $\Big)$ +2 $\Big)$ -2
   2 x 5 = 10 $\Big)$ +2 $\Big)$ -2
   2 x 6 = 12 $\Big)$ +2 $\Big)$ -2
   2 x 7 = 14 $\Big)$ +2 $\Big)$ -2
   2 x 8 = 16 $\Big)$ +2 $\Big)$ -2
   2 x 9 = 18 $\Big)$ +2 $\Big)$ -2
   2 x 10 = 20

   - Discuss **tasks 2-3, textbook p. 90 [3ʳᵈ p. 82]**. Students can use the page with dot stickers they made in the previous activity. Students should realize that until they have all the facts for "two times" memorized, they can use facts they already know to figure out the facts they don't yet know, rather than counting by twos from the beginning. If they know that 2 x 5 is 10, they can use that to figure out what 2 x 6 is. Six twos are two more than five twos.

Workbook Exercises 42-43

Activity 6.1c   **Doubles**

1. Relate the facts for ___ x 2 to the facts for 2 x _____.
   - Display a two by five array. Remind students that the array can be broken into either columns or rows. Ask students for two multiplication sentences. Write the addition sentence as well. Tell them that five plus five is the same as two fives, or five times two.
   - Tell them that we can call 5 + 5 or 5 x 2 "double five". Ask them to double some numbers up to 10 or 12, and write it as a multiplication equation. For example, ask them to double 4. 4 x 2 = 8.
   - They can also double doubles, for example, double 2, then double the answer to that.

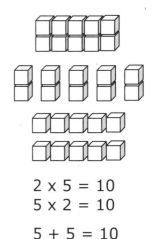

2 x 5 = 10
5 x 2 = 10

5 + 5 = 10

2. Have students do **tasks 5-8, textbook pp. 91-92 [3rd pp. 83-84]**.

3. Game (Double It)
   - Divide students into groups. Provide each group with four sets of number cards 1-10. Provide each student with a strip containing the even numbers through 20, and with 10 counters.
   - The cards are shuffled and turned face down in the middle. The players take turns drawing a card. They double the number on the card and cover the answer on their number strip (if it is not already covered). The first player to get all the numbers covered wins.

2	4	6	◯	10	12	14	16	18	20

Workbook Exercise 44

Activity 6.1d   **Multiplication facts for 2**

1. Provide practice in learning the multiplication facts for 2.
   - You can have students do the Mental Math 9 worksheet
   - You can have students play some of the games mentioned earlier in this guide (pp. 7-8), adapted for multiplication by 2, or play the "Fish for Twos" game below.

2. Have students do **Problems 1-5, Practice 6A, textbook p. 93 [3rd p. 85]**.

3. Game (Fish for Twos)
   - Divide students into groups. Give each group a set of fact cards for 2 x ___, ____ x 2, without answers on the back, and one set of answers (even numbers to 20). Cards should be shuffled.
   - The dealer deals 5 cards to each player and puts the rest face-down in the center. Players take turns asking another student for a particular card, "Do you have two times three?" If the other player does not have a card for the requested fact, the player whose turn it is draws a card from the center pile. If the other player does have the card, he must give it to the player who asked for it. The goal is to make sets of three containing both fact cards and the answer (e.g., 2 x 3, 3 x 2, and 6). Completed sets are put face-up in front of the player.

Workbook Exercise 45

Activity 6.1e   **Word problems**

1. Solve word problems which involve multiplication by 2.
   - Discuss **task 9, textbook p. 92 [3ʳᵈ p. 84]** and **problems 6-10, Practice 6A, textbook p. 93 [3ʳᵈ p. 85]**. Allow students to act out the problems using objects or drawing pictures.
   - You may also want to illustrate some of the problems using a number bond with equal parts. For example:
     - #6. Each bird has 2 wings. There are 6 birds. Draw a bar for each bird and write 2 in each bar. These are the parts. Draw a bar for the total. Tell them we need to find the total. Since the parts are equal, we can use multiplication.

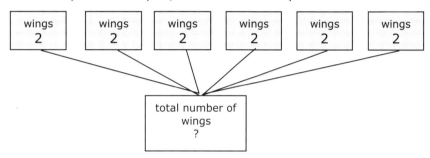

Workbook Exercise 46

Part 2: Multiplication Table of 3	6 sessions

Objectives

- Count by threes.
- Build multiplication table of 3.
- Memorize multiplication facts for 3.
- Write two multiplication equations for a rectangular array.
- Solve word problems involving multiplication by 3.

Materials

- Counters or other objects that can be displayed
- Dot stickers
- Hundreds board for students
- Connect-a-cubes for students
- Counters for students
- Hundreds board that can be displayed
- Number cube labeled with "x 2" and "x 3"
- Number cards 1-10, 4 sets for each group
- Fact cards

Homework

- Workbook Exercise 47
- Workbook Exercise 48
- Workbook Exercise 49
- Workbook Exercise 50
- Workbook Exercise 51
- Workbook Exercise 52
- Workbook Exercise 53
- Workbook Exercise 54
- Workbook Exercise 55

Notes

In this section, students will learn to count by threes, relate counting by threes to multiplication by three, and memorize the multiplication facts for 3 through 3 x 10. You may also wish to include 3 x 11 and 3 x 12.

Provide students with plenty of opportunity to practice the math facts for multiplication by 2 and 3.

Activity 6.2a   **Count by 3's**

1. Practice counting by threes
   - Provide each student with a sheet of dot stickers and an index card. Have them stick the dots on their papers in threes. Display ten sets of three on the board. Ask students to write the total number of stickers as they go down the rows of three next to each row (demonstrate on the board). Tell them we can count the number of objects by adding 3 to each number above it.
   - Have students practice counting their sets by threes. They can cover up all but the top two with an index card, say the next number, then move the card down to check.
   - Provide students with a hundreds board and opaque counters. Have the students cover up all the numbers from 1-30 except multiples of 3. Have them practice counting by threes forwards and backwards. Then have them cover up the multiples of three with the counters instead, leaving the others uncovered, and count by threes forwards and backwards by saying the numbers that are covered.
   - Have them practice without looking at the hundreds board until they can do it easily forwards and backwards.
   - Students should recognize whether a number is in the 3's sequence or not. Give them some numbers and ask them if the number is in the 3's sequence. For example, 12 is in the sequence, but 13 is not.

○	○	○	3
○	○	○	6
○	○	○	9
○	○	○	12
○	○	○	15
○	○	○	18
○	○	○	21
○	○	○	24
○	○	○	27
○	○	○	30

2. Write multiplication equations for situations involving counting by 3.
   - Display 4 sets of three. Ask how many there are. Point out that by counting by threes we are adding three each time. Ask them for a multiplication sentence showing that we have 3 times four.
   - Discuss the **textbook pp. 94-95 [3rd p. 86-87] and task 1, p. 95 [3rd p. 87].** Students supply the answers.

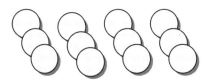

$$3 + 3 + 3 + 3 = 12$$

$$3 \times 4 = 12$$

Workbook Exercises 47-48

Activity 6.2b   **Triples**

1. Relate the facts for ___ x 3 to the facts for 3 x _____.
   - Display a three by five array. Remind students that the array can be broken into either columns or rows. Ask students for two multiplication sentences. Write the addition sentence as well. Remind them that if they know the answer to 3 x 5, then they also know the answer to 5 x 3.
   - Discuss **tasks 2-3, textbook p. 96 [3rd p. 88].**
   - Divide students into groups and provide each group with 30 connect-a-cubes. Call out a multiple of 3 between 3 and 30. Have students count out the cubes, arrange them in 3 rows, and write two multiplication equations for each.

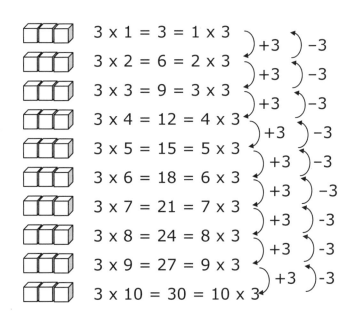

3 x 5 = 15
5 x 3 = 15

Workbook Exercise 49   5 + 5 + 5 = 15

Activity 6.2c   **Multiplication table for 3**

1. Build the multiplication table for 3.
   - Follow a procedure similar to activity 6.1b to show that we can build the multiplication facts for 3 by adding 3 to the previous fact. Include both multiplication equations for each fact, as in **task 4, textbook p. 96 [3rd p. 88].**
   - Discuss **tasks 5-6, textbook p. 97 [3rd p. 89].** Lead students to see that they can determine an unknown fact from a known fact by counting up or back by threes from the known fact.
   - Provide other examples. Include some for the related facts ___ x 3. For example:
     - 5 x 3 = 15
     - 6 x 3 = ?

3 x 1 = 3 = 1 x 3 } +3 } −3
3 x 2 = 6 = 2 x 3 } +3 } −3
3 x 3 = 9 = 3 x 3 } +3 } −3
3 x 4 = 12 = 4 x 3 } +3 } −3
3 x 5 = 15 = 5 x 3 } +3 } −3
3 x 6 = 18 = 6 x 3 } +3 } −3
3 x 7 = 21 = 7 x 3 } +3 } −3
3 x 8 = 24 = 8 x 3 } +3 } −3
3 x 9 = 27 = 9 x 3 } +3 } −3
3 x 10 = 30 = 10 x 3

Workbook Exercises 51-52

Activity 6.2d   **Multiplication facts for 3**

1. Provide practice in learning the multiplication facts for 3.
   - You can have students do the Mental Math 10-11 worksheets. These can also be done later, or used for daily practice. Show students how to fill in the multiplication table; the number that goes into each square is the answer when you multiply the number at the top of the column the square is in by the number at the left of the row the square is in.

- You can have students play some of the games mentioned earlier in this guide (pp. 7-8), adapted for multiplication by 3, or play and adaptation of the "Fish for Twos" game, or play the game below.

2. Have students do **Problems 1-5, Practice 6B, textbook p. 98 [3rd p. 90].**

3. Game
   - Divide students into groups. Provide each group with a copy of the Multiplication by 2 or 3 Game Board and counters, a different color for each student. Each group also needs four sets of number cards 1-10, and a number cube labeled with "x2" and "x3" (3 sides with "x2" and 3 sides with "x3") or a coin or counter labeled with "x2" on one side and "x3" on the other which they can flip.
   - Players take turns drawing a card and throwing the number cube or flipping the coin. They multiply the number on the card by the number on the cube (or coin) and place their counter on a square on the game board with the answer. The first student to get three counters in a row wins.

Workbook Exercises 50 and 53

Activity 6.2e   **Word problems**

1. Solve word problems which involve multiplication by 3.
   - Discuss **task 7, textbook p. 97 [3rd p. 89]**, and **problems 6-10, Practice 6B, textbook p. 98 [3rd p. 90].** Allow students to act out the problems using objects, or to draw pictures to help solve them. In discussing these problems, use language that emphasizes that there are a number of equal parts of given quantity. For example, in task 7, tell them that there are 7 equal parts, and each part has 3 kilograms. When we have a number of equal parts and the amount in each part (or group) we multiply.
   - You may also want to illustrate some of the problems using a part-whole model with equal parts. (Do not require students to draw the models.)

Workbook Exercise 54

Activity 6.2f   **Practice**

1. Have students do **Practice 6C, textbook p. 99 [3rd p. 91].** Let them discuss their solutions.

2. Recognize whether a number is part of the times 2 or the times 3 sequence.
   - Draw a diagram[1] such as the one shown here with some multiples of 3 in A, multiples of 2 in C, and multiples of both in the overlap B. Put a number that is neither a multiple of 2 or 3 outside the ovals.
   - See if your students can determine why each number is in a certain region. Ask them where they would put the rest of the numbers from 1 to 30.

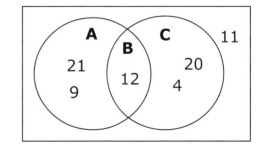

Workbook Exercise 55

---

[1] Diagrams like this are called Venn diagrams. (Your students do not have to know this.)

Part 3: Dividing by 2	3 sessions

Objectives

- Relate division facts to multiplication facts for 2.
- Memorize division facts for 2.
- Solve word problems involving division by 2.

Materials

- Transparent counters or other objects that can be displayed
- Connect-a-cubes for students
- Counters for students
- Number cards 1-10, four sets for each group
- Fact cards
- Index cards
- Additional word problems involving division by 2

Homework

- Workbook Exercise 56
- Workbook Exercise 57

Notes

In this section, students will relate multiplication facts for 2 to division by 2 and use the relationship to solve division problems. For example, if they have the division problem 12 ÷ 2 = ? they can think of ? x 2 = 12 and recall the appropriate multiplication fact. Eventually they should memorize the division facts.

Provide students with adequate fact practice. Include practice with multiplication facts, and any addition or subtraction facts still not mastered. Adapt some of the games given in this guide for multiplication. If appropriate, you could use computer software; adapt TV game shows, etc.

Mental Math 12

1. $20 \div 2 =$ _____

2. $14 \div 2 =$ _____

3. $4 \div 1 =$ _____

4. $18 \div 2 =$ _____

5. $5 \div 1 =$ _____

6. $6 \div 2 =$ _____

7. $16 \div 2 =$ _____

8. $18 \div 2 =$ _____

9. $8 \div 2 =$ _____

10. $14 \div 2 =$ _____

11. $12 \div 2 =$ _____

12. $6 \div 2 =$ _____

13. $12 \div 2 =$ _____

14. $4 \div 2 =$ _____

15. $20 \div 1 =$ _____

16. $10 \div 1 =$ _____

17. $16 \div 2 =$ _____

18. $1 \div 1 =$ _____

19. $20 \div 2 =$ _____

20. $12 \div 2 =$ _____

21. $14 \div 2 =$ _____

22. $9 \div 1 =$ _____

23. $10 \div 2 =$ _____

24. $8 \div 2 =$ _____

25. $2 \div 2 =$ _____

26. $10 \div 2 =$ _____

27. $16 \div 2 =$ _____

28. $18 \div 2 =$ _____

29. $4 \div 2 =$ _____

30. $123 \div 1 =$ _____

Activity 6.3a   Divide by 2

1. Relate division facts to multiplication facts for 2.
   - Display counters or other objects in two groups. Ask your students:
     - How many counters are in each group?
     - How many groups are there?
     - How many counters are there in all?
   - Write the equation 4 x 2 = 8. There are 4 counters in 2 equal groups.
   - Then write it with an arrow for the multiplication. Ask your students:
     - If we started with 8 counters and put them in 2 equal groups, how many would be in each group?
   - Write the equation 8 ÷ 2 = 4, and then show a reverse arrow for division.
   - Write some problems in the form of ___ x 2 = ____, such as 8 x 2 = 16. Have students copy the problem, draw similar arrow diagrams and then write the division fact.
   - Provide students with connect-a-cubes. Give then an even number and have them select that number and arrange the cubes in 2 rows. Have them write the multiplication and division equations:
     ___ x 2 = ___
     ___ ÷ 2 = ___
   - Discuss **textbook p. 100 [3rd p. 92]** and top of **p. 101 [3rd p. 93]**.
   - Have students do **tasks 1-2, textbook p. 101 [3rd p. 93]**.

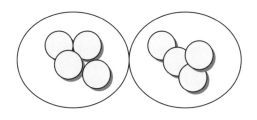

$4 \times 2 = 8$

$4 \xrightarrow{\times 2} 8$

$8 \div 2 = 4$

$\underline{\ \ 5\ \ } \times 2 = \underline{\ \ 10\ \ }$
$\underline{\ 10\ } \div 2 = \underline{\ \ 5\ \ }$

Workbook Exercise 56, #1

Activity 6.3b   Division facts for 2

1. Use multiplication facts to solve division problems.
   - Write the problems show on the right on the board. Have students copy them and fill in the blanks. Copying the equations, rather than just filling in a worksheet, can help the student pay attention to the pattern.
   - Point out that they can solve the division problems if they can think of the related multiplication problem. For example, with 16 ÷ 2, if they can remember *what* x 2 = 16, they will know the answer.
   - Write some division problems and have students write the related multiplication problems.

___ x 2 = 2	2 ÷ 2 = ___
___ x 2 = 4	4 ÷ 2 = ___
___ x 2 = 6	6 ÷ 2 = ___
___ x 2 = 8	8 ÷ 2 = ___
___ x 2 = 10	10 ÷ 2 = ___
___ x 2 = 12	12 ÷ 2 = ___
___ x 2 = 14	14 ÷ 2 = ___
___ x 2 = 16	16 ÷ 2 = ___
___ x 2 = 18	18 ÷ 2 = ___
___ x 2 = 20	20 ÷ 2 = ___

2. Provide practice in learning the division facts for 2.
   - You can have students do the Mental Math 12 worksheet. These can also be done later, or used for daily practice.

3. Have students do **problems 1-5, Practice 6D, textbook p. 104 [3ʳᵈ p. 96]**.

Workbook Exercise 56, #2

Activity 6.3c   **Word Problems**

1. Solve word problems which involve division by 2.
   - Discuss **tasks 3-6, textbook pp. 102-103 [3ʳᵈ pp. 94-95]**. Allow students to act out the problems.
   - Point out that in each of the problems we are given a total. Ask them for the total. Then ask them how many equal groups they have or how many must go into each group. You can illustrate the problems using a part-whole model. Do not require students to draw the part-whole models.
   - Write a division problem and have students make up a word problems to go along with it.

2. Have students do **problems 6-10, Practice 6D, textbook p. 104 [3ʳᵈ p. 96]**. Discuss their solutions.

Workbook Exercise 57

Part 4: Dividing by 3   5 sessions

Objectives

- Relate division facts to multiplication facts for 3.
- Memorize division facts for 3.
- Solve word problems involving division by 3.
- Review multiplication and division by 2 and 3.

Materials

- Counters or other objects that can be displayed
- Connect-a-cubes for students
- Counters for students
- Number cards 1-10, four sets for each group
- Fact cards

Homework

- Workbook Exercise 58
- Workbook Exercise 59
- Workbook Exercise 60
- Workbook Exercise 61
- Workbook Exercise 62

Notes

In this section, students will relate the multiplication facts for 3 to division by 3 and use the relationship to solve division problems. For example, if they have the division problem 12 ÷ 3 = ?, they can think of ? x 3 = 12 and recall the appropriate multiplication fact. They should eventually memorize the division facts.

Provide students with adequate fact practice. Include practice with multiplication facts, and any addition or subtraction facts not yet mastered.

Mental Math 13

1. $27 \div 3 =$ _____

2. $2 \div 2 =$ _____

3. $15 \div 3 =$ _____

4. $8 \div 2 =$ _____

5. $20 \div 2 =$ _____

6. $6 \div 3 =$ _____

7. $14 \div 2 =$ _____

8. $16 \div 2 =$ _____

9. $21 \div 3 =$ _____

10. $14 \div 2 =$ _____

11. $6 \div 3 =$ _____

12. $24 \div 3 =$ _____

13. $15 \div 3 =$ _____

14. $27 \div 3 =$ _____

15. $30 \div 3 =$ _____

16. $9 \div 3 =$ _____

17. $6 \div 2 =$ _____

18. $30 \div 3 =$ _____

19. $3 \div 3 =$ _____

20. $24 \div 3 =$ _____

21. $4 \div 2 =$ _____

22. $12 \div 3 =$ _____

23. $10 \div 2 =$ _____

24. $18 \div 3 =$ _____

25. $12 \div 2 =$ _____

26. $21 \div 3 =$ _____

27. $9 \div 3 =$ _____

28. $3 \div 3 =$ _____

29. $18 \div 3 =$ _____

30. $12 \div 3 =$ _____

Mental Math 14

1. $8 \div 1 =$ _____

2. $30 \div 3 =$ _____

3. $4 \times 2 =$ _____

4. $10 \times 3 =$ _____

5. $21 \div 3 =$ _____

6. $27 \div 3 =$ _____

7. $6 \times 3 =$ _____

8. $2 \times 9 =$ _____

9. $12 \div 2 =$ _____

10. $3 \times 8 =$ _____

11. $3 \times 7 =$ _____

12. $15 \div 3 =$ _____

13. $7 \times 2 =$ _____

14. $9 \times 1 =$ _____

15. $2 \times 6 =$ _____

16. $3 \times 2 =$ _____

17. $10 \times 2 =$ _____

18. $1 \times 3 =$ _____

19. $3 \div 3 =$ _____

20. $5 \times 3 =$ _____

21. $27 \div 3 =$ _____

22. $7 \times 3 =$ _____

23. $6 \div 3 =$ _____

24. $2 \times 3 =$ _____

25. $20 \div 2 =$ _____

26. $8 \div 2 =$ _____

27. $18 \div 3 =$ _____

28. $6 \div 2 =$ _____

29. $18 \div 2 =$ _____

30. $6 \times 2 =$ _____

Mental Math 15

1. 8 x 2 = _____

2. 9 x 3 = _____

3. 14 ÷ 2 = _____

4. 12 ÷ 3 = _____

5. 8 x 3 = _____

6. 3 x 7 = _____

7. 21 ÷ 3 = _____

8. 9 x 2 = _____

9. 4 ÷ 2 = _____

10. 2 x 2 = _____

11. 9 x 3 = _____

12. 16 ÷ 2 = _____

13. 2 x 7 = _____

14. 5 x 2 = _____

15. 1 x 324 = _____

16. 3 x 3 = _____

17. 16 ÷ 2 = _____

18. 9 ÷ 3 = _____

19. 24 ÷ 3 = _____

20. 2 x 8 = _____

21. 18 ÷ 2 = _____

22. 12 ÷ 3 = _____

23. 18 ÷ 3 = _____

24. 6 ÷ 1 = _____

25. 14 ÷ 2 = _____

26. 4 x 3 = _____

27. 3 x 9 = _____

28. 2 ÷ 2 = _____

29. 1 x 2 = _____

30. 84 ÷ 1 = _____

Division by 2 or 3 Game Board

3	8	2	4	6	☆
4	9	1	5	7	3
7	5	10	8	6	10
9	8	2	1	10	3
4	6	1	5	6	7
2	10	5	8	7	2
☆	8	9	3	4	1

Multiplication and Division by 2 or 3 Game Board

3	8	4	18	6	☆
24	9	6	21	7	3
7	30	10	15	8	2
12	8	2	1	10	12
4	6	10	5	9	14
30	3	5	16	6	2
☆	8	18	27	4	1

Activity 6.4a   **Divide by 3**

1. Relate division facts to multiplication facts for 3.
    *   Display counters or other objects in three groups. Use a procedure similar to that given in activity 6.3a to show how division by 3 is related to multiplication by 3.
    *   Write some problems in the form of ___ x 3 = ____, such as 9 x 3 = 27. Have students copy the problem, draw similar arrow diagrams and then write the division fact.
    *   Provide students with connect-a-cubes. Give them a multiple of 3 and have them arrange the cubes in 3 rows. Have them write the multiplication and division equations:
        ○   ___ x 3 = ___
        ○   ___ ÷ 3 = ___
    *   Discuss **textbook p. 105 [3rd p. 97]** (top of page).
    *   Have students do **task 1, textbook p. 105 [3rd p. 97]**.

    Workbook Exercise 58, #1

$4 \times 3 = 12$

$4 \xrightarrow{\times 3} 12$

$12 \div 3 = 4$

$4 \underset{\div 3}{\overset{\times 3}{\rightleftarrows}} 12$

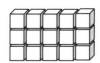

$\underline{5} \times 3 = \underline{15}$
$\underline{15} \div 3 = \underline{5}$

Activity 6.4b   **Division facts for 3**

1. Use multiplication facts to solve division problems.
    *   Write the problems shown on the right on the board. Have students copy them and fill in the blanks.
    *   Point out that they can solve the division problems if they can think of the related multiplication problem. For example, with 18 ÷ 3, if they can remember *what* x 3 = 18, they will know the answer.
    *   Give students some division problems and have them tell you the related multiplication problem.

2. Provide practice in learning the division facts for 3.
    *   You can have students do the Mental Math 13 worksheet. These can also be done later, or used for daily practice.

3. Have students do **problems 1-5, Practice 6E, textbook p. 107 [3rd p. 99]**.

    Workbook Exercise 58, #2

____ x 3 = 3	3 ÷ 3 = ____
____ x 3 = 6	6 ÷ 3 = ____
____ x 3 = 9	9 ÷ 3 = ____
____ x 3 = 12	12 ÷ 3 = ____
____ x 3 = 15	15 ÷ 3 = ____
____ x 3 = 18	18 ÷ 3 = ____
____ x 3 = 21	21 ÷ 3 = ____
____ x 3 = 24	24 ÷ 3 = ____
____ x 3 = 27	27 ÷ 3 = ____
____ x 3 = 30	30 ÷ 3 = ____

Activity 6.4c   **Word Problems**

1. Solve word problems which involve division by 3.
   - Discuss **tasks 2-3, textbook p. 106 [3ʳᵈ p. 98]**. Allow students to act out the problems.
   - Write a division problem and have students make up a word problems to go along with it.

2. Have students do **problems 6-10, Practice 6E, textbook p. 107 [3ʳᵈ p. 99]**. Discuss their solutions.

Workbook Exercise 59

Activity 6.4d   **Practice**

1. Have students do **Practice 6F, textbook p. 108 [3ʳᵈ p. 100]**. Discuss their solutions.

2. Students can do the Mental Math 14-15 worksheets.

3. Game
   - Divide students into groups. Provide counters for each group. Each player uses a different color counter.
     - Game 1 – Provide each group with the Division by 2 or 3 Game Board. Each group uses four sets of division cards, two sets for division by 2, and two sets for division by 3. Use cards without answers on the back.
     - Game 2 – Provide each group with the Multiplication and Division by 2 or 3 Game Board. Each group uses one set of multiplication fact cards for 2, one set of multiplication facts cards for 3, one set of division fact cards for 2, and one set of division fact cards for 3. Use cards without answers on the back.
   - Cards are shuffled and placed in the middle. Players take turns turning over a card and placing a marker on the square with the answers. The first player to get three in a row vertically, horizontally, or diagonally wins.

Workbook Exercises 60-63

Review 4

Objectives

- Review previous topics.

Suggested number of sessions: 4

	Objectives	Textbook	Workbook	Activities
77-80	▪ Review	p. 109, Review B p. 110, Review C	Review 6	R.4

Activity R.4 Review

1. Discuss the problems in **Reviews B-C, textbook pp. 109-112 [3rd pp. 101-104]**.

2. Provide additional review as necessary.

3. Have students play any favorite games or do other fact practice for addition and subtraction as well as multiplication and division by 2 and 3.

Workbook Review 6

Mental Math Worksheets Answer Key

Mental Math 1					Mental Math 2					Mental Math 3			
1.	10	18.	8		1.	4	18.	1		1.	4	18.	5
2.	11	19.	6		2.	2	19.	1		2.	4	19.	5
3.	13	20.	16		3.	2	20.	3		3.	7	20.	5
4.	13	21.	7		4.	5	21.	3		4.	8	21.	8
5.	10	22.	18		5.	2	22.	1		5.	2	22.	6
6.	17	23.	13		6.	3	23.	1		6.	7	23.	9
7.	16	24.	5		7.	3	24.	4		7.	9	24.	4
8.	12	25.	15		8.	2	25.	3		8.	6	25.	9
9.	12	26.	10		9.	2	26.	3		9.	6	26.	8
10.	8	27.	16		10.	5	27.	4		10.	9	27.	9
11.	9	28.	12		11.	4	28.	5		11.	9	28.	7
12.	15	29.	12		12.	2	29.	8		12.	6	29.	9
13.	11	30.	9		13.	5	30.	4		13.	3	30.	8
14.	14	31.	14		14.	7	31.	2		14.	8	31.	5
15.	11	32.	10		15.	6	32.	6		15.	7	32.	8
16.	4	33.	9		16.	2	33.	7		16.	3	33.	7
17.	11	34.	7		17.	6	34.	1		17.	6	34.	7

Mental Math 4					Mental Math 5					Mental Math 6			
1.	442	16.	431		1.	25	16.	90		1.	21	16.	73
2.	72	17.	209		2.	57	17.	80		2.	63	17.	74
3.	83	18.	674		3.	40	18.	41		3.	43	18.	79
4.	4	19.	181		4.	58	19.	86		4.	56	19.	69
5.	378	20.	811		5.	27	20.	30		5.	23	20.	26
6.	62	21.	297		6.	30	21.	24		6.	6	21.	10
7.	63	22.	112		7.	70	22.	27		7.	16	22.	6
8.	342	23.	582		8.	69	23.	77		8.	66	23.	69
9.	594	24.	80		9.	70	24.	20		9.	85	24.	14
10.	101	25.	841		10.	71	25.	80		10.	23	25.	46
11.	61	26.	612		11.	73	26.	39		11.	41	26.	29
12.	398	27.	804		12.	44	27.	62		12.	42	27.	40
13.	648	28.	628		13.	62	28.	60		13.	43	28.	30
14.	59	29.	700		14.	63	29.	90		14.	44	29.	30
15.	197	30.	290		15.	33	30.	100		15.	48	30.	66

Mental Math 7

1.	5	16.	15
2.	55	17.	150
3.	455	18.	350
4.	14	19.	353
5.	34	20.	10
6.	334	21.	100
7.	10	22.	800
8.	70	23.	807
9.	670	24.	206
10.	661	25.	450
11.	667	26.	499
12.	363	27.	472
13.	570	28.	112
14.	577	29.	220
15.	283	30.	1000

Mental Math 8

1.	8	16.	5
2.	58	17.	50
3.	958	18.	56
4.	6	19.	55
5.	56	20.	550
6.	256	21.	558
7.	142	22.	460
8.	137	23.	469
9.	904	24.	310
10.	994	25.	280
11.	985	26.	802
12.	986	27.	440
13.	443	28.	446
14.	645	29.	456
15.	355	30.	642

Mental Math 9

1.	2	16.	10
2.	6	17.	7
3.	6	18.	20
4.	14	19.	16
5.	18	20.	18
6.	8	21.	14
7.	16	22.	8
8.	10	23.	4
9.	12	24.	16
10.	3	25.	14
11.	18	26.	18
12.	12	27.	5
13.	8	28.	20
14.	6	29.	40
15.	20	30.	60

Mental Math 10

x	1	2	3	4	5	6	7	8	9	10
1	1	2	3	4	5	6	7	8	9	10
2	2	4	6	8	10	12	14	16	18	20
3	3	6	9	12	15	18	21	24	27	30
4	4	8	12							
5	5	10	15							
6	6	12	18							
7	7	14	21							
8	8	16	24							
9	9	18	27							
10	10	20	30							

Mental Math 11

1.	3	16.	12
2.	12	17.	16
3.	12	18.	3
4.	18	19.	21
5.	6	20.	24
6.	21	21.	15
7.	15	22.	18
8.	24	23.	27
9.	30	24.	15
10.	27	25.	6
11.	18	26.	24
12.	9	27.	9
13.	14	28.	30
14.	10	29.	60
15.	21	30.	90

Mental Math 12

1.	10	16.	10
2.	7	17.	8
3.	4	18.	1
4.	9	19.	10
5.	5	20.	6
6.	3	21.	7
7.	8	22.	9
8.	9	23.	5
9.	4	24.	4
10.	7	25.	1
11.	6	26.	5
12.	3	27.	8
13.	6	28.	9
14.	2	29.	2
15.	20	30.	123

Mental Math 13

1.	9	16.	3
2.	1	17.	3
3.	5	18.	10
4.	4	19.	1
5.	10	20.	8
6.	2	21.	2
7.	7	22.	4
8.	8	23.	5
9.	7	24.	6
10.	7	25.	6
11.	2	26.	7
12.	8	27.	3
13.	5	28.	1
14.	9	29.	6
15.	10	30.	4

Mental Math 14

1.	8	16.	6
2.	10	17.	20
3.	8	18.	3
4.	30	19.	1
5.	7	20.	15
6.	9	21.	9
7.	18	22.	21
8.	18	23.	2
9.	6	24.	6
10.	24	25.	10
11.	21	26.	4
12.	5	27.	6
13.	14	28.	3
14.	9	29.	9
15.	12	30.	12

Mental Math 15

1.	16	16.	9
2.	27	17.	8
3.	7	18.	3
4.	4	19.	8
5.	24	20.	16
6.	21	21.	9
7.	7	22.	4
8.	18	23.	6
9.	2	24.	6
10.	4	25.	7
11.	27	26.	12
12.	8	27.	27
13.	14	28.	1
14.	10	29.	2
15.	324	30.	84

Textbook Answer Key

Unit 1 - Numbers to 1000

Part 1: Looking Back (pp. 6-9)

1. (a) 45   (b) 45
   (c) 45   (d) 45
2. 100
3. (a) 26   (b) 43   (c) 57
4. (a) 66   (b) 64
   (c) 75   (d) 55
5. (a) 67   (b) 63
   (c) 85   (d) 45
6. (a) 81   (b) 82
   (c) 90   (d) 100
   (e) 79   (f) 78
   (g) 70   (h) 60

Part 2: Comparing Numbers (pp. 10-11)

1. (a) >   (b) <
   (c) >   (d) <
   (e) <   (f) >
2. (a) 39   (b) 30
   (c) 56   (d) 98
3. 50, 59, 90, 95

Practice 1A (p. 12)

1. (a) forty-four   (b) fifty-five
   (c) ninety-five   (d) one hundred
2. (a) 6 tens 5 ones (b) 4 tens
   (c) 7 tens 8 ones (d) 9 tens 7 ones
3. (a) 66   (b) 81
   (c) 53   (d) 70
4. (a) 54   (b) 73
5. (a) 100   (b) 49
6. (a) 89   (b) 35
7. (a) >   (b) <
   (c) >   (d) >
   (e) >   (f) <

Part 3: Hundreds, Tens, And Ones (pp. 13-20)

1. (a) 346   (b) 437
2. 236
3. (a) 258   (b) 470   (c) 809
4. (c) 10
5. 10
6. (a) 100   (b) 1000
7. 6, 2, 3
8. (a) 467   (b) 250   (c) 306

9. (a) 254   (b) 133   (c) 241
10. (a) 800   (b) 490   (c) 570

Practice 1B (p. 21)

1. (a) three hundred thirty
   (b) one hundred forty-four
   (c) two hundred fifty-five
   (d) six hundred eight
2. (a) 6 hundreds 4 tens 5 ones
   (b) 7 hundreds 2 tens
   (c) 4 hundreds 9 ones
   (d) 9 hundreds
3. (a) 704   (b) 540
   (c) 304   (d) 820
4. (a) >   (b) <
   (c) >   (d) >
5. (a) 99, 410, 609
   (b) 104, 140, 401, 410
6. (a) 300   (b) 779
7. (a) 472   (b) 790
8. (a) 699   (b) 505

Unit 2 - Addition and Subtraction

Part 1: Meanings of Addition and Subtraction (pp. 22-27)

1. 6
2. 12, 12, 7, 5
3. 12, 12, 9, 3
4. (a) 4   (b) 4
5. (a) 6   (b) 6
6. 56
7. 14
8. 45, 32, 45, 13
9. 39, 39
10. 56, 56
11. 38, 38
12. 16; 16

Part 2: Addition without Renaming (pp. 28-30)

1. (a) 5   (b) 50   (c) 500
2. 57
3. (a) 69   (b) 79   (c) 58
   (d) 69   (e) 94   (f) 99
4. 285
5. 387
6. (a) 134   (b) 290   (c) 197
   (d) 589   (e) 576   (f) 595
7. 189, 189, 189

Part 3: Subtraction without Renaming (p. 31-33)

1. (a) 4   (b) 40   (c) 400
2. 24
3. (a) 74   (b) 38
   (c) 60   (d) 15
   (e) 22   (f) 10
4. 214
5. 224
6. (a) 406   (b) 78
   (c) 512   (d) 207
   (e) 220   (f) 326
7. 235, 235, 235

Practice 2A (p. 34)

1. (a) 37   (b) 76   (c) 88
2. (a) 61   (b) 39   (c) 51
3. (a) 77   (b) 99   (c) 98
4. (a) 20   (b) 36   (c) 22
5. (a) 89   (b) 40   (c) 5
6. 25
7. 67
8. 23
9. 99
10. $5

Practice 2B (p. 35)

1. (a) 359   (b) 168   (c) 599
2. (a) 862   (b) 622   (c) 441
3. (a) 193   (b) 567   (c) 597
4. (a) 528   (b) 294   (c) 224
5. (a) 488   (b) 502   (c) 607
6. 299
7. 364
8. 113
9. 236
10. (a) 229   (b) 21

Part 4: Addition with Renaming (pp. 36-40)

1. (a) 13   (b) 69
   (c) 73   (d) 130
   (e) 609   (f) 730
2. (a) 42   (b) 80
   (c) 86   (d) 83
   (e) 70   (f) 100
3. 361
4. (a) 323   (b) 231
   (c) 572   (d) 656
   (e) 770   (f) 390
5. 390

6. (a) 492   (b) 671   (c) 763
   (d) 881   (e) 610   (f) 990
7. 619
8. (a) 352   (b) 644   (c) 448
   (d) 724   (e) 500   (f) 309
9. 527
10. (a) 617   (b) 826
    (c) 608   (d) 808
    (e) 618   (f) 929
12. (a) 334   (b) 521   (c) 703
13. 421
14. (a) 621   (b) 602   (c) 600
16. (a) 733   (b) 921

Practice 2C (p. 41)

1. (a) 35   (b) 40   (c) 53
2. (a) 63   (b) 80   (c) 90
3. (a) 100   (b) 100   (c) 100
4. (a) 107   (b) 115   (c) 119
5. (a) 115   (b) 129   (c) 109
6. 50
7. 108
8. 16
9. 44
10. (a) 74   (b) 90

Practice 2D (p. 42)

1. (a) 314 (b) 439 (c) 435
2. (a) 445 (b) 580 (c) 693
3. (a) 853 (b) 951 (c) 894
4. (a) 629 (b) 834 (c) 895
5. (a) 377 (b) 483 (c) 650
6. 240
7. 325
8. 228
9. 215
10. $161

Part 5: Subtraction with Renaming (pp. 43-47)

1. (a) 4   (b) 5   (c) 35
   (d) 40   (e) 50   (f) 350
2. (a) 24   (b) 32   (c) 39
   (d) 28   (e) 26   (f) 28
3. 225
4. (a) 345   (b) 473   (c) 528
   (d) 645   (e) 702   (f) 804
5. 318
6. (a) 214   (b) 325   (c) 258
   (d) 214   (e) 507   (f) 106
7. 665

8. (a) 272   (b) 371   (c) 462
    (d) 646   (e) 540   (f) 56
9. 245
10. (a) 370   (b) 168
    (c) 213   (d) 321
    (e) 350   (f) 80
11. 353
12. (a) 275   (b) 375   (c) 553
13. 186
14. (a) 363   (b) 364   (c) 377
15. 272
16. (a) 362   (b) 424   (c) 65

Practice 2E (p. 48)

1. (a) 32   (b) 38   (c) 36
2. (a) 27   (b) 29   (c) 25
3. (a) 18   (b) 48   (c) 45
4. (a) 9   (b) 7   (c) 1
5. (a) 5   (b) 5   (c) 5
6. 32
7. 83
8. 69
9. $34
10. $70

Practice 2F (p. 49)

1. (a) 320   (b) 432   (c) 540
2. (a) 77   (b) 308   (c) 425
3. (a) 162   (b) 207   (c) 207
4. (a) 391   (b) 394   (c) 394
5. (a) 177   (b) 416   (c) 77
6. 140
7. 522
8. 18
9. 155
10. (a) 258   (b) 562

Practice 2G (p. 50)

1. (a) 79   (b) 77   (c) 99
2. (a) 59   (b) 40   (c) 6
3. (a) 108   (b) 80   (c) 109
4. (a) 33   (b) 35   (c) 5
5. (a) 100   (b) 101   (c) 107
6. 59
7. 106
8. Team B; 16
9. (a) 35   (b) 43

Practice 2H (p. 51)

1. (a) 210   (b) 413   (c) 320
2. (a) 199   (b) 288   (c) 699

3. (a) 301   (b) 260   (c) 47
4. (a) 284   (b) 555   (c) 607
5. (a) 358   (b) 337   (c) 96
6. 705
7. 117
8. $34
9. 117
10. (a) $68   (b) Watch: $76

Unit 3 - Length

Part 1: Measuring Length in Meters (pp. 52-54)

3. (a) 11 m   (b) 3 m
4. 12 m
5. 36 m

Part 2: Measuring Length in Centimeters (pp. 55-58)

4. Line A- 12 cm, Line B- 12cm
    They are the same.
5. Papaya Rd.- shortest, Rambutan Rd.- longest

US Part 3: Measuring Length in Yards and Feet (pp. 59-60)

4. String B; 3

US Part 4: Measuring Length in Inches (pp. 61-62)

4; 4; 12
Line B is longer.

Practice 3A (US p. 63) [3rd p. 59]

1. (a) 294   (b) 399   (c) 500
2. (a) 571   (b) 502   (c) 960
3. (a) 384   (b) 187   (c) 378
4. (a) 129   (b) 204   (c) 319
5. (a) 800   (b) 178   (c) 694
6. 900 m
7. 55 cm
8. US: 64 yd   3rd: 64 m
9. 88 cm

Unit 4 - Weight

Part 1: Measuring Weight in Kilograms (US pp. 64-67) [3rd pp. 60-63]

2. (a) 2 kg   (b) 3 kg
3. Lighter
4. More

5. 9 kg
6. (a) B; 2 kg (b) 10 kg
7. (a) C   (b) A   (c) 10 kg

Part 2: Measuring Weight in Grams (US pp. 68-69) [3rd pp. 64-65]

1. (a) 400 g   (b) 600 g
2. (a) 350 g   (b) 230 g

US Part 3: Measuring Weight in Pounds (pp. 70-71)

2. heavier
3. (a) the one on the left; 2 lb
    (b) 16 lb

US Part 4: Measuring Weight in Ounces (US pp. 72-73)

1. 6   10

Practice 4A (US p. 74) [3rd p. 66]

1. (a) 261   (b) 408   (c) 533
2. (a) 637   (b) 856   (c) 930
3. (a) 193   (b) 287   (c) 320
4. (a) 32   (b) 480   (c) 586
5. (a) 554   (b) 623   (c) 535
6. (a) Durian   (b) 350 g
7. (a) 67 kg   (b) 106 kg
8. (a) 220 g   (b) 500 g
9. (a) 750 g   (b) 660 g

Review A (US p. 75) [3rd p. 67]

1. (a) 659   (b) 715   (c) 850
2. (a) 977   (b) 660   (c) 1000
3. (a) 402   (b) 782   (c) 810
4. (a) 500   (b) 350   (c) 32
5. (a) 184   (b) 625   (c) 398
6. 13 m
7. 181 cm
8. 245 g
9. (a) 26 kg   (b) 60 kg

Unit 5 - Multiplication and Division

Part 1: Multiplication (US pp. 76-78) [3rd pp. 68-70]

1. 20
2. 30
3. (a) 21   (b) 36
4. (a) 8; 8   (b) 15; 15

Practice 5A (US p. 79) [3rd p. 71]

1. 24
2. 10
3. 18
4. 15

Part 2: Division (US pp. 80-85) [3rd pp. 72-77]

2. 5; 5
3. 6; 6
5. 5; 5
6. 6; 6
7. 18; 18; 9; 2
8. 32; 32; 8; 4

Practice 5B (US p. 86) [3rd p. 78]

1. 6
2. 4
3. 10
4. 7

Practice 5C (US p. 87) [3rd p. 79]

1. 21; 21; 7; 3
2. 3
3. 20
4. 7

Unit 6 - Multiplication Tables of 2 and 3

Part 1: Multiplication Table of 2 (US pp. 88-92) [3rd pp. 80-84]

1. (a) 4   (b) 18
2. (a) 6   (b) 8
3. 12
4. 8; 10; 12; 14; 16; 18; 20
5. (a) 10; 10   (b) 14; 14
6. (a) 16; 16   (b) 18; 18
7. (a) 8; 10; 12; 14; 16; 18; 20
8. 6; 2; 9
9. 12; 12

Practice 6A (US p. 93) [3rd p. 85]

1. (a) 6   (b) 8   (c) 4
2. (a) 2   (b) 18   (c) 16
3. (a) 12   (b) 14   (c) 20
4. (a) 10   (b) 6   (c) 8
5. (a) 18   (b) 12   (c) 14
6. 12
7. 20
8. $10

9. 8 kg
10. 16 m

Part 2: Multiplication Table of 3 (US pp. 94-97) [3ʳᵈ pp. 86-89]

1. (a) 12   (b) 24
2. 18; 18
3. 2; 3; 8
4. 12; 15; 18; 21; 24; 27; 30
    3; 6; 9; 12; 15; 18; 21; 24; 27; 30
5. 18
6. 24
7. 21 kg

Practice 6B (US p. 98) [3ʳᵈ p. 90]

1. (a) 3   (b) 6   (c) 12
2. (a) 18   (b) 21   (c) 24
3. (a) 12   (b) 15   (c) 30
4. (a) 21   (b) 27   (c) 9
5. (a) 24   (b) 30   (c) 18
6. 12
7. 21
8. 24 kg
9. US: 18 yd   3ʳᵈ: 18 m
10. 30

Practice 6C (US p. 99) [3ʳᵈ p. 91]

1. (a) 2   (b) 3   (c) 8
2. (a) 10   (b) 12   (c) 18
3. (a) 16   (b) 27   (c) 9
4. (a) 20   (b) 24   (c) 21
5. (a) 14   (b) 15   (c) 18
6. 15
7. $14
8. 18
9. 18 m
10. 30 lb

Part 3: Dividing by 2 (US pp. 100-103) [3ʳᵈ pp. 92-95]

1. (a) 4   (b) 7
2. 8; 8 10; 10
3. 4; 4
4. 7; 7
5. 6; 6
6. 9; 9

Practice 6D (US p. 104) [3ʳᵈ p. 96]

1. (a) 8   (b) 10   (c) 4
2. (a) 4   (b) 5   (c) 2
3. (a) 12   (b) 18   (c) 16

4. (a) 6   (b) 9   (c) 8
5. (a) 7   (b) 1   (c) 10
6. 10
7. 9
8. $10
9. 8 m
10. 7

Part 4: Dividing by 3 (US pp. 105-106) [3ʳᵈ pp. 97-98]

1. 8; 8   5; 5
    7; 7   9; 9
2. 10; 10
3. 8; 8

Practice 6E (US p. 107) [3ʳᵈ p. 99]

1. (a) 12   (b) 18   (c) 15
2. (a) 4   (b) 6   (c) 5
3. (a) 27   (b) 21   (c) 24
4. (a) 9   (b) 7   (c) 8
5. (a) 3   (b) 2   (c) 10
6. 10
7. $6
8. 5
9. $27
10. 8

Practice 6F (US p. 108) [3ʳᵈ p. 100]

1. (a) 5   (b) 7   (c) 4
2. (a) 3   (b) 5   (c) 4
3. (a) 6   (b) 8   (c) 10
4. (a) 6   (b) 8   (c) 7
5. (a) 9   (b) 10   (c) 9
6. 8 cm
7. 10
8. $14
9. 8
10. $6

Review B (US pp. 109-110) [3ʳᵈ pp. 101-102)]

1. (a) 606   (b) 855   (c) 440
2. (a) Two hundred fifty
    (b) Seven hundred forty-four
    (c) Three hundred seven
    (d) Nine hundred twenty-two
3. (a) 213   (b) 449
    (c) 799   (d) 325
4. (a) 15, 18, 21, 27
    (b) 470, 460, 450, 430
5. 909, 912, 928, 930

6. (a) 8   (b) 8
    (c) 90   (d) 9
    (e) 70   (f) 5
    (g) 100   (h) 50
7. (a) 4 kg   (b) 350
8. (a) brush   (b) 1 cm
9. 15
10. 153
11. 128 cm
12. 8

Review C (US pp. 111-112) [3rd pp. 103-104]

1. (a) 408   (b) 590   (c) 555
2. (a) 78   (b) 703   (c) 734
3. (a) 18   (b) 24   (c) 16

4. (a) 9   (b) 8   (c) 8
5. (a) 7   (b) 10   (c) 10
6. (a) 689   (b) 505
    (c) 40   (d) 0
7. (a) <   (b) >
    (c) >   (d) <
8. (a) 130   (b) 120
9. 268
10. $31
11. 18
12. $9
13. 915
14. $210
15. 9

Workbook Answer Key

Exercise 1

1. (a) 37; 37; 37
   (b) 58; 58; 58
   (c) 94; 94; 94
2. (a) 49   (b) 62
   (c) 80   (d) 100
3. (a) 2; 4   (b) 4; 2; 2
   (c) 6; 7; 67
4. (a) 49   (b) 52
   (c) 66   (d) 100
5. (a) 46   (b) 67
   (c) 58   (d) 93
   (e) 81   (f) 25
6. (a) fifty
   (b) sixty-four
   (c) twenty-one
   (d) ninety-nine
   (e) thirty-two
   (f) one hundred

Exercise 2

1. (a) 77   (b) 75
   (c) 86   (d) 66
2. (a) 78   (b) 74
   (c) 96   (d) 56
3. (a) 40   (b) 73   (c) 100
   (d) 73   (e) 76   (f) 74
4. (a) 56   (b) 57
   (c) 65   (d) 75
   (e) 54   (f) 53
   (g) 45   (h) 35
5. (a) 71   (b) 72
   (c) 80   (d) 90
   (e) 69   (f) 68
   (g) 60   (h) 50
6. (a) 49   (b) 50
   (c) 58   (d) 68
   (e) 47   (f) 46
   (g) 38   (h) 28

Exercise 3

1. (a) 50   (b) 59   (c) 28
   (d) 70   (e) 87   (f) 100
2. (a) 45   (b) 87   (c) 63
   (d) 100   (e) 70   (f) 57
3. (a) 23   (b) 24
   (c) 29   (d) 78
   (e) 54   (f) 87
   (g) 60   (h) 98

4. (a) 31   (b) 50   (c) 45
   (d) 56   (e) 15   (f) 36
5. (a) 67, 76, 78, 87
   (b) 90, 82, 79, 66
6. (a) greater than [>]
   (b) less than [<]
   (c) greater than [>]
   (d) less than [<]
   (e) less than [<]
   (f) greater than [>]
   (g) greater than [>]
   (h) less than [<]
   (i) less than [<]
   (j) greater than [>]

Exercise 4

1. (a) 214   (b) 346   (c) 305
   (d) 472   (e) 563   (f) 660
   (g) 790   (h) 307
2. 129 219 355 535 553 740 704
3. (a) 175   (b) 253
   (c) 240   (d) 407
4. 611   309   293   390
   90   6   500   60

Exercise 5

1. (a) 460   (b) 303   (c) 339
2. (a) 56   (b) 325   (c) 761
   (d) 430   (e) 606

Exercise 6

1. 320   440   541   792   404
   514   729   958   985
2. 109   207   320   411
   515 1000   940   861
3. eight hundred four
   four hundred forty-one
   three hundred thirteen
   seven hundred ninety-nine
   six hundred fifty-five
   five hundred sixty
4. six hundred eighty
   eight hundred twenty one
   nine hundred nine
   two hundred fifty-three
   three hundred twelve

Exercise 7

1. (a) 335   (b) 420   (c) 506
2. (a) 573   (b) 774
   (c) 508   (d) 840

Exercise 8

1. (a) 10; 10; 8; 2
   (b) 11; 11; 7; 4
   (c) 13; 13; 7; 6
   (d) 14; 14; 6; 8
   (e) 17; 17; 14; 3
   (f) 19; 19; 9;10
   (g) 25; 25; 20; 5
   (h) 19; 19; 13; 6

Exercise 9

1. (a) 5; 5   (b) 7; 7   (c) 6; 6
2. (a) 8; 8   (b) 7; 7   (c) 9; 9
   (d) 8; 8   (e) 4; 4   (f) 8; 8

Exercise 10

1. 14
2. 13
3. 47
4. (a) 34   (b) 12
   (c) 71   (d) 2

Exercise 11

1. (a) 8; 8
   (b) 8; 80
   (c) 8; 800
2. (a) 7; 70; 700
   (b) 10; 100; 1000
3. Across   Down
   A. 56   A. 58
   B. 49   C. 98
   D. 57   E. 55
   F. 89   G. 99
   H. 75   H. 72
   J. 68   I. 38
   K. 48   J. 67
   M. 77   K. 46
   N. 76   L. 69
   O. 95   N. 74
   P. 64

Exercise 12

1. A. 598   C. 396   E. 787
   H. 189   M. 856   N. 495
   O. 655   R. 789   T. 971
   MEET ME AT THE CORNER

2. 849   667   835
   789   798   366
   488   569   987
   Sentosa Island
3. 466
4. 188
5. 546

Exercise 13

1. (a) 6; 6
   (b) 6; 60
   (c) 6; 600
2. (a) 4; 40; 400
   (b) 9; 90; 900
3. Across   Down
   A. 75   B. 53
   C. 24   D. 43
   F. 32   E. 72
   H. 27   G. 21
   J. 14   I. 74
   L. 88   K. 48
   O. 50   M. 84
   P. 36   N. 53
   Q. 2

Exercise 14

1. 657   713   908
   120   326   549
   834   245   400
2. A. 305   B. 172
   D. 532   C. 256
   E. 407   F. 621
   H. 410   G. 50
   I. 261   J. 813   Fish
3. 25
4. 222
5. 421

Exercise 15

1. (a) 13; 33; 533
   (b) 10; 50; 250
   (c) 13; 130; 530
   (d) 10; 100; 400
   (e) 17; 77; 277
   (f) 10; 90; 390
2. (a) 71   (b) 81
   (c) 145   (d) 640
   (e) 150   (f) 100
   (g) 310   (h) 500
3. A. 81   B. 92   D. 93
   H. 72   I. 82   P. 95
   R. 84   T. 70   Y. 80
   HAPPY BIRTHDAY

Exercise 16

1. 981   373   471
   793   872   376
   750   675   890
2. 865   435   826
   327   519   787
   900   627   318
   airplane

Exercise 17

1. 91   56   355
   131   523   480
   824   403   852
   rabbit
2. 250
3. 357
4. 522

Exercise 18

1. C. 820   D. 325   E. 901   G. 501
   H. 373   L. 640   T. 902   Z. 860
2. 301   540   764
   642   700   816
   830   723   915
   615   702   927
3. 221
4. 831
5. 624

Exercise 19

1.   327   735
   691   731   308
       815   725
   GOOD MORNING
2. 250
3. 906
4. 215

Exercise 20

1. C. 15   D. 38   E. 37
   I. 39   M. 4   N. 6
   O. 46   S. 28   T. 26
   IT DOES NOT COME TO ME
2. A. 735   B. 343   E. 26
   L. 363   M. 333
   N. 116   R. 745   U. 540
   AN UMBRELLA
3. 148
4. 98
5. 107

Exercise 21

1. A. 454   B. 154   C. 295
   D. 81   E. 522
   F. 352   G. 685   H. 774
   The treasure is hidden below the rain tree.
2. 573
3. 192
4. 217

Exercise 22

US
1. B. 253   S. 568   D. 759
   E. 75   A. 217   O. 649
   O. 579   K. 489   R. 277
   READ BOOKS
3rd
1. A. 253   E. 568   G. 759
   I. 75   N. 217   O. 649
   P. 579   R. 489   S. 277
   MY SINGAPORE
2. 41   198   269   194   195
   512   298   77   78   374
3. 257
4. 76
5. 55

Exercise 23

1. 268   138
   362   546   26
   659   26   485   485
   IN THE WELL
2. 331
3. 218
4. 28

Exercise 24

1. A. 81   C. 775   H. 1000
   I. 327   M. 378   R. 530
   S. 277   S. 723   T. 638
   MERRY CHRISTMAS
2. 138
3. 72
4. 85

Review 1

1. 123   215   649   307
   506   780   808   451
2. (a) 89   (b) 367
   (c) 534   (d) 140
3. (a) four hundred fifty-five

(b) seven hundred forty-four
(c) eight hundred fifty
(d) nine hundred three
4. (a) greater than [>]
   (b) less than [<]
   (c) greater than [>]
   (d) greater than [>]
   (e) greater than [>]
   (f) greater than [>]
5. (a) 58; 88; 99; 59
   (b) 360; 500; 20; 450
6. (a) 482   (b) 92   (c) 652

Exercise 26

2. (a) 3   (b) 10
3. (a) 8   (b) 11
   (c) 9   (d) 12
4. (a) 11   (b) 9
   (c) 2   (d) 4
   (e) brush
   (f) US: clothespin   3rd: clothes peg
5. (a) m   (b) m   (c) cm
   (d) cm   (e) m   (f) cm
   (g) cm   (h) cm
   (i) m   (j) cm

Exercise 27

2. (a) 12   (b) 9   (c) 3
3. 12; 4
4. (a) 8   (b) 11   (c) 10
   (d) B   (e) A

US Exercise 28

1. (a) ft   (b) in.   (c) yd
   (d) in.   (e) ft
2. Yellow rod

3rd Exercise 28

1. Check the lengths of the lines.
2. AB is 7 cm long.
   (a) The line should be 10 cm long.
   (b) The line should be 5 cm long.]

Review 2

1. (a) 99   (b) 8; 2
   (c) 6; 4; 7 (c) 5; 0; 3
2. 899, 904, 908, 910
3. 995   998   999
   975   978   979
   965
        957   958

4. (a) greater than [>]
   (b) less than [<]
   (c) greater than [>]
   (d) greater than [>]
   (e) less than   [<]
   (f) greater than [>]
5. (a) 157   (b) 873
   (c) 209   (d) 920
6. 223
7. (a) 30   (b) 42
   (c) 8   (d) 100
8. (a) 1000   (b) 800   (c) 690
   (d) 308   (e) 242
9. (a) 349   (b) 758
   (c) 604   (d) 580
10. (a) two hundred twenty
    (b) four hundred thirty-one
    (c) eight hundred sixty-nine
    (d) nine hundred forty-four
11. (a) 19   (b) 398   (c) 40

Exercise 29

3. papaya   grapes   bananas [durian]
4. (a) 2   (b) 3
   (c) 7   (d) 4
   (e) 1   (f) 5

Exercise 30

2. (a) 130   (b) 90
   (c) 220   (d) 40
3. (a) 700   (b) 200
   (c) 500   (d) 350
   (e) 200   (f) 50

Review 3

1. (a) 192   (b) 209
   (c) 370   (d) 405
   (e) 66   (f) 605
   (g) 398   (h) 909
2. (a) 90   (b) 7
   (c) 700   (d) 200
3. 62 + 38 = 100   38 + 62 = 100
   100 − 38 = 62   100 − 62 = 38
4. (a) 389   (b) 500
   (c) 416   (d) 402
   (e) 1000   (f) 55
5. (a) 528   (b) 369   (c) 951
   (d) 369   (e) 634
6. 452
7. 800
8. 115

9. 644
10. $246
11. 665

Review 4

1. pear shape
2. 420   204
   431   134
   754   457
   432   234
   954   459
   330   303
3. (a) 689   (b) 40
   (c) 80   (d) 200
4. 12; 10
5. (a) 130   (b) 80
6. 17
7. 509
8. 154
9. 123
10. 580
11. 78

Exercise 31

1. (a) 24; 24   (b) 24; 24   (c) 20; 20
2. (a) 14; 14   (b) 14; 14   (c) 20; 20

Exercise 32

1. 10
2. 8
3. 18
4. 24
5. 28

Exercise 33

1. 20; 20
2. 12; 12
3. 24; 24
4. 24; 24
5. 18; 18
6. 50; 50

Exercise 34

1. (a) 15; 15   (b) 14; 14   (c) 18; 18
2. (a) 30; 30   (b) 28; 28
   (c) 48; 48   (d) 30; 30

Exercise 35

1. (a) 6   (b) 8   (c) 4
2. (a) 5   (b) 5

3. (a) 6   (b) 6
4. 4

Exercise 36

1. (a) 6   (b) 7   (c) 3
2. $32 \div 4 = 8$; 8
3. $30 \div 6 = 5$; 5

Exercise 37

1. (a) 3   (b) 4   (c) 6
2. (a) 3   (b) 3
3. (a) 7   (b) 7
4. 3

Exercise 38

1. (a) 2   (b) 4   (c) 3
2. $18 \div 2 = 9$; 9
3. $15 \div 3 = 5$; 5

Exercise 39

1. (a) 6; 6   (b) 5; 5
2. (a) 3; 2   (b) 7; 3
   (c) 5; 4   (d) 9; 2
3. (a) $35 \div 7 = 5$; $35 \div 5 = 7$
   (b) $18 \div 6 = 3$; $18 \div 3 = 6$
4. $6 \times 4 = 24$ $4 \times 6 = 24$
   $24 \div 6 = 4$ $24 \div 4 = 6$

Review 5

1. $24 + 17 = 41$ $17 + 24 = 41$
   $41 - 17 = 24$ $41 - 24 = 17$
2. $8 \times 2 = 16$ $2 \times 8 = 16$
   $16 \div 2 = 8$ $16 \div 8 = 2$
3. (a) 730; 710; 690
   (b) 492; 692; 892
4. (a) 465   (b) 261   (c) 397
   (d) 742   (e) 44   (f) 665
   (g) 738   (h) 199
5. (a) 957   (b) 980
   (c) 980   (d) 957
6. $20 \div 5 = 4$; 4
7. $18 \div 6 = 3$; 3
8. $4 \times 5 = 20$; 20
9. $124 - 48 = 76$; 76
10. 112
11. 158

Exercise 40

1. 2; 4; 6; 8; 10; 12; 14; 16; 18; 20
2. 8; 10; 12; 14; 16; 18; 20
3. 4; 6; 8; 10; 12; 14; 16; 18; 20

Exercise 41

1. 6; 6
2. 8; 8
3. 10; 10
4. 12; 12
5. 2 x 7 = 14; 14
6. 2 x 8 = 16; 16

Exercise 42

1. (a) 8   (b) 12   (c) 14; 16
2. 6; 8; 10; 12; 14; 16; 18; 20

Exercise 43

1. 4; 6; 2; 12; 8; 18; 10; 14; 20; 16

Exercise 44

1. (a) 12; 12   (b) 14; 14
   (c) 18; 18   (d) 20; 20
2. 20; 2 x 10   10; 2 x 5   14; 2 x 7
   6; 2 x 3   18; 2 x 9   12; 2 x 6
   16; 2 x 8

Exercise 45

1. down: 8; 16; 6; 18
          20; 4; 12
          10; 14; 2
2. across: 6; 16; 12
           8; 18; 14
           20; 10; 8
           16; 18; 12

Exercise 46

1. 16; 16
2. 6 x 2 = 12; 12
3. 3 x 2 = 6; 6
4. 14
5. 10
6. 8

Exercise 47

1. 3; 6; 9; 12; 15; 18; 21; 24; 27; 30
2. 12; 15; 18; 21; 24; 27; 30

Exercise 48

1. 6; 9; 12; 15; 18; 21; 24; 27; 30
2. (a) 4; 8; 12; 16
   (b) 6; 15; 21; 27
   (c) $6; $10; $14; $18; $20
   (d) $9; $12; $18; $24; $30

Exercise 49

1. 6; 6
2. (a) 9   (b) 12; 12   (c) 15; 15
3. (a) 18; 18   (b) 21; 21
   (c) 24; 24   (d) 27; 27

Exercise 50

1. 3; 3 x 1   12; 3 x 4   24; 3 x 8
   6; 3 x 2   27; 3 x 9
   21; 3 x 7 18; 3 x 6
2. (down) 2 x 3; 3 x 3; 4 x 3; 5 x 3
          3 x 6; 7 x 3; 3 x 8; 3 x 9; 10 x 3

Exercise 51

1. (a) 12   (b) 18   (c) 24; 27
2. 9; 12; 15; 18; 21; 24; 27; 30

Exercise 52

1. (a) 12   (b) 18   (c) 30; 27
2. 24; 21; 18; 15; 12; 9; 6; 3

Exercise 53

1. 12   24   18
   9   21   27
   15   12   27
   30   24   18

Exercise 54

1. 10 x 3 = 30; 30
2. 24
3. 15
4. 21
5. 27
6. 18

Exercise 55

1. 6   12
   18   24
   30   10
   8   15
   14   21
   27   12
2. 3 x 8 = 24; 24
3. 21
4. 14
5. 20
6. 16
7. 18

Exercise 56

1.   1   2
              8
      5   8
      3   9
      3   9
      10   4
      10   4
      6   7
      6   7
2. 1; 5; 2; 4; 8; 6; 10; 7; 9

Exercise 57

1. 8 ÷ 2 = 4; 4
2. 5
3. 6
4. 10
5. 7
6. 8

Exercise 58

1.   1
              2
      4   4
      5   5
      3   3
      10   10
      7   7
      9   9
      6   6
      8   8
2. (down) 6; 8; 4; 9
    10; 5; 3; 1; 7

Exercise 59

1. 24 ÷ 3 = 8; 8
2. 6
3. 4
4. 5
5. 9
6. 7

Exercise 60

1. 9 ÷ 3   12 ÷ 2
    6 ÷ 3   15 ÷ 3
    2 ÷ 2   20 ÷ 2
    12 ÷ 3   16 ÷ 2
    14 ÷ 2   27 ÷ 3
2. 2   7   6   7   9
    D   O   N   O   T

10   1   8   9   3
W   A   S   T   E

9   4   5   3
T   I   M   E
DO NOT WASTE TIME

Exercise 61

1. 8
2. 9
3. 6
4. 6
5. 9
6. 8

Exercise 62

1. 10   18   4   8
    12   7   10   14
    16   7   9   27
2. 5
3. 21
4. 12
5. 18
6. 8
7. 9

Review 6

1. (a) eight hundred fifty-seven
    (b) six hundred forty-four
2. 6 x 3 = 18   18 ÷ 6 = 3
    3 x 6 = 18   18 ÷ 3 = 6
3. (a) 456 − 50 = 406 or 456 − 406 = 50
    (b) 275 + 325 = 600 or 325 + 275 = 600
    (c) 3 x 9 = 27 or 9 x 3 = 27
    (d) 18 ÷ 9 = 2 or 18 ÷ 2 = 9
4. 980; 1000
    988
    957
    946; 956; 986; 996
5. (a) 7; 7   (b) 6; 6
6. 829; 831; 846; 852
7. (a) 7   (b) 50
8. 440   96   230
   103   450   636
   330   35   840
   320   455   518
9.   8   20   10
    10   18   8
    12   9   6
     6   7   12
     4   14   19
     8   16   20

10. 367
11. 24
12. 8
13. 165
14. 9
15. 453

Review 7

1. (a) 550   (b) 929
2. (a) seven hundred forty-four
   (b) eight hundred six
3. (a) less than [<]
   (b) less than   [<]
   (c) greater than [>]
   (d) greater than [>]
   (e) greater than [>]
   (f) less than [<]
4. (a) 879   (b) 760   (c) 504
   (d) 90   (e) 607   (f) 10
5. (a) 3   (b) 12
6. (a) 4   (b) 12
US: 7. (a) lb   (b) in.
       (c) oz   (d) yd   (e) ft

3rd: 7. (a) kg   (b) cm
        (c) g   (d) m
8. (a) 473   (b) 516
   (c) 852   (d) 800
   (e) 340   (f) 126
   (g) 358   (h) 575
9. (a) 6   (b) 15
   (c) 21   (d) 18
   (e) 9   (f) 10
   (g) 16   (h) 27
   (i) 1   (j) 2
   (k) 5   (l) 9
   (m) 1   (n) 5
   (o) 8   (p) 7
10. 6
11. 18
12. 15
13. 236
14. 131
15. 135